Rescuing Darwin

is the title essay of a wide-ranging project exploring the extent and nature of evolutionary and non-evolutionary beliefs in the UK today and their perceived relationship with theism and atheism.

The project is managed and run by Theos, the public theology think tank, in partnership with the Faraday Institute for Science and Religion.

It includes an essay on Darwinism and theism in modern Britain, an extended interview with the philosopher Mary Midgley, and two major independent research studies, conducted by the polling company ComRes, and the ethnographic social research agency ESRO.

Rescuing Darwin was made possible by a generous grant from the John Templeton Foundation.

For more details visit **www.theosthinktank.co.uk**

Nick Spencer is Director of Studies at Theos, the public theology think tank.
Denis Alexander is Director of the Faraday Institute for Science and Religion.

Theos

The public theology think tank

what Theos is

Theos is a public theology think tank which exists to undertake research and provide commentary on social and political arrangements. We aim to impact opinion around issues of faith and belief in society. We were launched in November 2006 with the support of the Archbishop of Canterbury, Dr Rowan Williams, and the Cardinal Archbishop of Westminster, Cardinal Cormac Murphy-O'Connor. Our first report *"Doing God": A Future for Faith in the Public Square* examined the reasons why faith will play an increasingly significant role in public life.

what Theos stands for

Society is embarking on a process of de-secularisation. Interest in spirituality is increasing across Western culture. Faith is on the agenda of both government and the media. In the arts, humanities and social sciences there are important intellectual developments currently taking place around questions of values and identity. Theos speaks into this new context. Our perspective is that faith is not just important for human flourishing and the renewal of society, but that society can only truly flourish if faith is given the space to do so. We reject notions of a sacred-secular divide.

what Theos works on

Theos undertakes research across a wide range of subject areas. We analyse social and political change and offer interesting new angles and alternative perspectives on the issues that matter.

what Theos provides

Theos undertakes its work through:

- a research and publishing programme,
- conferences, seminars and lectures,
- outreach to university, college and school students,
- news, information and analysis to media companies and other opinion formers, with a one-stop information line available to journalists,
- regular email bulletins,
- other related activities.

In addition to our independently driven work, Theos provides research, analysis and advice to individuals and organisations across the private, public and not-for-profit sectors. Our unique position within the think tank sector means that we have the capacity to develop proposals that carry values - with an eye to demonstrating what really works. Our staff and consultants have strong public affairs experience, an excellent research track record and a high level of theological literacy. We are practised in campaigning, media relations, detailed policy development and effecting policy change.

www.theosthinktank.co.uk

Rescuing Darwin

God and evolution in Britain today

by Nick Spencer and Denis Alexander

Published by Theos in 2009
© Theos

ISBN: 0 9554453 5 3
ISBN-13: 978 0 9554453 5 4

For further information and subscription details please contact:

Theos
Licence Department
34 Buckingham Palace Road
London
SW1W 0RE
United Kingdom

T 020 7828 7777
E hello@theosthinktank.co.uk
www.theosthinktank.co.uk

contents

introduction

Charles Darwin dedicated an entire chapter of *The Origin of Species* to detailing the problems with his theory. It was typical of his honesty and integrity that he should not gloss over such "a crowd of difficulties" but expose them to a critical audience.[1] And, in 1859, not only was there a highly critical audience but there were genuine and serious questions relating to his theory.

In 2009, the evidence for evolution by natural selection is overwhelming, although of course the theory itself continues to evolve as new data come to light. The fossil record, although incomplete, firmly supports the theory, revealing impressive series of transitional forms. More recently, advances in genetics have hugely strengthened evolution, to the extent that, in scientific circles at least, it is now incontestable.

But only, it seems, in scientific circles. According to a recent, detailed quantitative research study commissioned by Theos and conducted by the polling company ComRes, only 37% of people in the UK believe that Darwin's theory of evolution is "beyond reasonable doubt". 32% say that Young Earth Creationism ("the idea that God created the world sometime in the last 10,000 years") is either definitely or probably true, and 51% say that Intelligent Design ("the idea that evolution alone is not enough to explain the complex structures of some living things, so the intervention of a designer is needed at key stages") is either definitely or probably true.

> *Only 37% of people in the UK believe that Darwin's theory of evolution is "beyond reasonable doubt".*

If those figures don't quite add up (and they don't) it is because although many people (around a quarter) actively reject evolution, at least as many again are simply sceptical or unsure, and inclined to hedge their bets. Either way, 150 years after the publication of *The Origin of Species*, in the country of the author's birth, this is a sorry state of affairs.

The reasons are complex but they seem to rest on the misconception that science and religion are somehow rival descriptions of the way the world works. According to this view, God and evolution are "competing explanation[s] for facts about the universe and life",[2] the creation stories of Genesis are a form of (bad) proto-science, and evolution by natural selection is somehow able to "solve the mystery of our existence".[3]

The fact that the answer to that mystery, at least according to Darwin's more prominent modern disciples, is that there is no ultimate purpose or meaning to life further exacerbates the problem. Being told they are accidents of evolution, "robots", "survival machines" of secondary importance, whose moral principles are illusory, whose mind is merely a colony of memes, and who inhabit a universe with "no purpose, no evil and no good" has limited appeal to most people.[4]

If either of these views were correct – if Genesis chapters 1-3 were written to provide a scientific account of human origins or if evolution were "reductionism incarnate"[5] – then we would just have to live with the resultant battle between tough-minded, atheistic evolutionists on the one side and soft-hearted, obscurantist believers on the other.

But they are not correct, nor, as far as we can tell, reflective of Darwin's own position. Darwin had lost his Christian faith by the time he came to write *The Origin of Species* but given how much that faith had rested on the natural theology of William Paley, which his theory undermined, that is not entirely surprising. No longer a Christian, he remained a deist for many years, before slipping into agnosticism in his final decade. He was clear, however, that he was never an atheist and he explicitly rejected the idea that evolution necessitated atheism. Moreover, in marked contrast to some of his modern disciples, he engaged with everyone, even those who disagreed with him, in a spirit of respect and courtesy – a spirit that is sorely missing from the modern debate.

Both Darwin's position and his spirit of engagement need to be rescued from the crossfire of a battle between the militant godly and militant godless who, though poles apart on so many issues, seem to agree that evolution threatens belief in God.

Only when rescued, and restored as a *scientific* rather than (anti-)theological theory, will the popular reception of evolution match the scientific one. And only then will Charles Darwin be seen, 200 years after his birth – not as a kind of scientific Moses leading his benighted people out of the intellectual slavery of superstition; nor as the iniquitous architect of a spurious theory that led to atheism, materialism and genocide – but rather as one of the most brilliant scientists in history.

introduction - references

1. Charles Darwin, *The Origin of Species* (John Murray, 1859), chapter 6.

2. Richard Dawkins, "A Reply to Poole", in *Science & Christian Belief* 7 (1995) pp. 45-50.

3. Richard Dawkins, *The Blind Watchmaker* (Longman, 1986), p. xiv.

4. Richard Dawkins, *River Out of Eden* (Weidenfeld & Nicolson, 1995), p. 155.

5. Daniel Dennett, *Darwin's Dangerous Idea* (Simon & Schuster, 1995), p. 82.

Darwin and God

"It seems to me absurd to doubt that a man may be an ardent Theist & an evolutionist." So wrote Charles Darwin to John Fordyce in 1879. "In my most extreme fluctuations," he continued, "I have never been an atheist in the sense of denying the existence of a God."[1]

Darwin died three years later, without changing his mind. "You have expressed my inward conviction," he told the author William Graham in one of his last letters, "that the Universe is not the result of chance."[2]

Despite what such opinions might suggest, Darwin was not a Christian. He had lost his religious faith thirty years earlier and, by this stage of his life, he was not even a theist. "The mystery of the beginning of all things is insoluble by us," he wrote in his *Autobiography*, "and I for one must be content to remain an Agnostic."[3]

> *"It seems to me absurd to doubt that a man may be an ardent Theist & an evolutionist."*

Darwin had serious reasons for his agnosticism. He was not simply apathetic. He did not, however, like metaphysical speculation and hated religious controversy. "I hardly see how religion & science can be kept…distinct," he once wrote to J Brodie Innes, the vicar of Downe with whom he shared a lifelong friendship. "But…there is no reason why the disciples of either school should attack each other with bitterness."[4]

before the *Beagle*

Darwin was born on 12 February 1809. His family background, on both sides, was wealthy, illustrious and vaguely unconventional. His maternal grandfather was a Unitarian and his paternal one a scientifically-minded rationalist who was, at the time, Britain's foremost evolutionist. His father, Robert, was a highly-respected country doctor and probably an atheist; his mother shared her family's Unitarianism.

Darwin attended the local Unitarian chapel until his mother died when he was eight. He subsequently boarded at Shrewsbury Grammar school before joining his brother in Edinburgh to study medicine. Neither took to medicine, with Charles already too interested in the study of nature (not to mention hunting, shooting and fishing).

Few letters survive from his Edinburgh days but those that do reveal a lukewarm religiosity. "Dear Charles I hope you read the bible", chided his sister Caroline, "and not only because you think it wrong not to read it." "I often regret myself that when I was younger & fuller of pursuits & high spirits I was not more religious," she confided.[5]

Vexed by his son's lack of medical ambition, Robert Darwin insisted Charles find useful employment. He proposed the Anglican Church. Darwin hesitated, unsure of what he actually believed. He took time to read through some weighty theological tomes, such as John Pearson's 1659 *Exposition of the Creed*, and duly persuaded and deeming himself "orthodox" agreed to ordination.

> *"Dear Charles I hope you read the bible and not only because you think it wrong not to read it."*

There is no doubt that Darwin *was* orthodox, but that orthodoxy was of a particular kind: logical, rational, demonstrable. Christianity was, for the young Darwin, an argument to be proved. Orthodoxy meant being able to assent to key Christian doctrines.

His time at Cambridge encouraged this view. Cambridge theology was, during this period, heavily influenced by William Paley, the former Archdeacon of Carlisle. Ordinands were compelled to study his *Principles of Moral and Political Philosophy* and *View of the Evidences of Christianity*, with Darwin remarking, "I am convinced that I could have written out the whole of the *Evidences* with perfect correctness."[6]

He also read (by choice) Paley's *Natural Theology* which argued succinctly that nature contains "every manifestation of design…Design must have had a designer…That designer must have been a person. That person is God."[7]

Darwin was impressed and Paleyian natural theology became the keystone of his Christian faith.

Despite (or perhaps because of) this, Darwin's Christianity seems to have been no more secure in Cambridge than it had been in Edinburgh. His friend JM Herbert, who was also training for the ministry, recalled "an earnest conversation" with him "about going into Holy Orders". During the ordination service the Bishop would ask candidates, "Do you trust that you are inwardly moved by the Holy Spirit?" Herbert remembered Darwin asking him whether he could "answer in the affirmative" when thus asked. Herbert replied that he could not, to which Darwin replied, "Neither can I, and therefore I cannot take orders."

the view from the *Beagle*

He did not take orders, although more by chance than design. In the summer of 1831, the opportunity arose of travelling the world on the surveying ship, *Beagle*. Darwin seized it. For the next five years, he lived as the self-financing, gentlemanly companion of Captain Robert FitzRoy, as the ship worked around the coastal waters of South America before heading west across the Pacific.

Darwin's time on the *Beagle* did not seriously challenge his ordered, propositional, Paleyian faith but it did disturb the foundations. Darwin experienced earthquakes and volcanic eruptions that seemed to suggest the earth was indifferent, rather than tailored, to human needs. He encountered people on the Tierra del Fuego who were shockingly barbarous, even animalistic. Perhaps the world was not as benign as natural theology assumed? Perhaps the line between humans and other species was thinner, more permeable, than comfortable Anglican ordinands imagined?

the origin of *The Origin*

He returned to England in late 1836 and immediately embarked on an extraordinary intellectual journey.

His autobiography, written forty years later, concentrates his loss of faith into this period and offers three broad reasons for that loss: doubts about the Bible ("no more to be trusted than the sacred books of the Hindoos"); moral objections (the Old Testament writers "attribute to God the feelings of a revengeful tyrant"); and philosophical problems ("the more we know of the fixed laws of nature the more incredible do miracles become").

Darwin undoubtedly stumbled over each of these issues but it is highly unlikely they all occurred to him during this period. Biblical criticism, for example, had hardly made a mark in Britain before 1840. In reality, Darwin probably fashioned his autobiography so as to bring together all his doubts into a single chapter and timeframe, which he placed during a period of intense and destabilising intellectual speculation.

Darwin captured that speculation, exploring the origin of species, in a series of notebooks, which also describe his attempts to accommodate his new theory with his existing philosophical and theological beliefs.

Sometimes this was easy. Evolution wrecked the idea that God had made each species separately. But then, why should such an idea threaten theism? How much more appealing was a continuous process of law-governed evolution than the idea "that since the time of the Silurian [God] has made a long succession of vile molluscous animals"?[8]

More challenging was the idea that humans may not, in fact, be so very different from other species. "Man – wonderful man…with divine face turned towards heaven…he is not a deity, his end under present form will come…he is no exception," he wrote in one notebook, sounding like an Old Testament prophet.

Perhaps most seriously, there was the question of suffering. This was not a new problem, as Darwin acknowledged, but it was exacerbated by the duration and apparent cruelty of natural selection. His theory replaced Paley's "happy world… [of] delighted existence" with the brutal one in which a "dreadful but quiet war of organic beings [was] going on in the peaceful woods & smiling fields."[9] For a faith that was based primarily on William Paley, this was a serious blow.

Emma Wedgwood, Darwin's cousin who became his wife in January 1839, recognised this. She was brought up a Unitarian but by the time she married Charles, was a thoughtful, orthodox Christian. Despite advice from his father to the contrary, Charles confided his religious doubts to her in the summer before they married. She took them in her stride and their diverging religious opinions did not stop them forging a strong and intimate marriage that lasted over four decades.

Darwin's confession of his doubts to Emma, before they were married, gives the lie to those who suggest that Darwin simply hid his atheism for fear of upsetting his wife. "He is the most open, transparent man I ever saw, and every word expresses his real thoughts," Emma told her aunt.[10]

For her part, she quickly understood how his mind worked and wrote him several short but brilliantly perceptive letters in 1838-39, discussing their religious differences. Although entreating him to read chapter 13 of John's gospel – "It is so full of love…& devotion & every beautiful feeling" – she did not try to "convert" him, recognising that "honest & conscientious doubts cannot be a sin."[11] Emma did, however, realise that the *way* he looked at the world, so profoundly shaped by his long hours of observation and experimentation, was making religious belief difficult:

> May not the habit in scientific pursuits of believing nothing till it is proved, influence your mind too much in other things which cannot be proved in the same way, & which if true are likely to be above our comprehension.[12]

It was to prove a prescient observation.

the death of a daughter

Darwin's theory challenged his Christian faith but he seems to have remained a theist with Christian inclinations throughout the 1840s. The key question was whether "the highest good, which we can conceive, the creation of the higher animals" justified the "death, famine, rapine, and the concealed war of nature" of natural selection.[13] Darwin's answer, in the first sketch of *The Origin*, written in 1842, appeared to be yes – in theory.

But then the question of suffering moved from theory to terrible reality. His eldest daughter, Annie, had long suffered from ill-health and in 1851 he took her to Malvern for water-therapy, a mid-Victorian craze. He returned home to his heavily-pregnant wife but was soon summoned back; Annie had contracted a fever. Darwin returned instantly, to be faced with a changed child. "You would not in the least recognize her," he told his wife, "with her poor hard, sharp pinched features; I could only bear to look at her by forgetting our former dear Annie."

The following week was the worst of his life. Unable to eat, Annie slowly wasted away. She showed signs of recovery, and then faded. The doctors remained quietly confident. Darwin sat, holding her hand, alternately overjoyed then distraught. Eventually, she died, aged ten.

Most Victorian families lost children – Darwin himself lost two others in infancy – but Annie was his favourite and he had witnessed every last, degrading moment of her short life. The experience nearly destroyed him. It certainly destroyed the final remnants of his faith. He wrote a short, painfully moving account of her life, and then never spoke about her again.

deistic theism

Darwin remained a theist and, contrary to what some Christians claimed (and claim), wrote *The Origin of Species* with scientific rather than (anti-)theological intent. "Dr Pusey [the Oxford divine] was mistaken in imagining that I wrote the Origin with any relation whatever to Theology," he later wrote to Henry Ridley.[14] "I should have thought that this would have been evident to anyone who has taken the trouble to read the book."

His theism was based on the conviction that "I cannot…be contented to view this wonderful universe & especially the nature of man, & to conclude that everything is the result of brute force," – although properly speaking this was closer to deism, the belief that God created the universe and then withdrew into silent indifference.[15]

Despite being able to write in his autobiography that "whether the world as a whole is a good or a bad one…my judgment [is] happiness decidedly prevails," it was clearly suffering that was the issue for Darwin.[16]

"I cannot persuade myself that a beneficent & omnipotent God would have designedly created the Ichneumonidæ with the express intention of their feeding within the living bodies of caterpillars," he wrote to his Christian friend at Harvard, Professor Asa Gray.[17]

the death of an agnostic

This was how he remained – confused – right into his final decade. "My theology is a simple muddle," he told Joseph Hooker in 1870. "I cannot look at the Universe as the result of blind chance, yet I can see no evidence of beneficent Design."[18]

Such confusion was a source of his agnosticism – although not the only one. In his final years, he began to doubt whether the human mind, being evolved from earlier primates, was even capable of understanding such questions. "Can the mind of man, which has, as I fully believe, been developed from a mind as low as that possessed by the lowest animal, be trusted when it draws such grand conclusions?" he wrote in his *Autobiography*.[19]

Thus his agnosticism was of the profoundest kind. Not only did he not know about God but he didn't know whether he *could* know. "I think that generally (& more and more so as I grow older) but not always, that an agnostic would be the most correct description of my state of mind," he confided to John Fordyce.[20]

That agnosticism did not prevent him living a life that bore an uncanny resemblance to that of a liberal, Anglican clergyman. Living most of his life in a former country parsonage, he served as treasurer of Downe's Coal and Clothing Club, set up and administered the Downe Friendly Society, was a member of the parish council, regularly contributed to the village Sunday School, had his children christened at Downe church, gave generously towards its upkeep, was an honorary member of the South American Missionary Society to which he made small donations, and spoke warmly of Christianity's good influence on society. "Your services have done more for the village in a few months than all our efforts for many years," he told the local evangelist James Fegan.[21]

In spite of his wishes to be buried at Downe, he was interred at Westminster Abbey when he died in 1882. The honour would have been inconceivable twenty years earlier and stands as testimony to two key facts.

The first, as we shall see in the next chapter, is that by the 1880s evolution was no longer particularly controversial. In a remarkably short space of time educated Christian opinion in Britain and America had happily accommodated the new theory.

The second was that Darwin himself was universally recognised not only as a brilliant natural scientist but also as an honourable and courteous human being. In spite of his loss of faith and the pain he suffered in seeing three of his children die young, he remained as respectful to those who retained religious beliefs as he was to fellow agnostics. It was dogmatism, whether religious or atheistic, that upset him. "Why should you be so aggressive?" he asked the atheist Edward Aveling, shortly before he died. "Is anything gained by trying to force these new ideas upon the mass of mankind?"[22]

chapter 1 - references

1. Letter to John Fordyce, 7 May 1879.

2. Letter to William Graham, 3 July 1881.

3. Charles Darwin, *The Autobiography of Charles Darwin 1809-1882* (Collins, 1958; repr. Penguin, 2002), p. 94.

4. Letter to JB Innes, 27 November 1878.

5. Caroline Darwin to Charles Darwin, 22 March 1826.

6. Darwin, *Autobiography*, p. 59.

7. William Paley, *Natural Theology* (Oxford University Press, 2006).

8. Notebook D.

9. Paley, *Natural Theology*, p. 456; Charles Darwin, Notebook E.

10. HE Litchfield, ed., *Emma Darwin, A Century of Family Letters, 1792-1896* (John Murray, 1915), Volume 2, p. 6.

11. Emma Wedgwood to Charles Darwin, 21–22 November 1838.

12. Emma Darwin to Charles Darwin, c. February 1839.

13. Francis Darwin ed., *The Foundations of The Origin of Species. Two essays written in 1842 and 1844* (Cambridge University Press, 1909), p. 52.

14. Letter to Henry Ridley, 28 November 1878.

15. Letter to Asa Gray, 22 May 1860.

16. Darwin, *Autobiography*, p. 88.

17. Letter to Asa Gray, 22 May 1860.

18. Letter to Joseph Hooker, 12 July 1870.

19. Darwin, *Autobiography*, p. 93.

20. Letter to John Fordyce, 7 May 1879.

21. Letter to James Fegan, between December 1880 and February 1881.

22. Edward Aveling, *The Religious Views of Charles Darwin* (Freethought Publishing Company, 1883), p. 5.

2

God after Darwin

There is an enduring mythology that, after 1859, evolution faced a concerted campaign of opposition from the Church. Nothing could be further from the truth. Like any significant new scientific theory, Darwin's "big idea" received criticism, much of it justified, and Darwin painstakingly revised subsequent editions of *The Origin of Species* to take such comments into account.

In reality, what is most noticeable about the initial reactions to Darwin's theory is their sheer diversity. Many scientists, religious and secular, incorporated the theory into their work rapidly and with the minimum of fuss. By the mid-1860s questions about Darwin's theory were already appearing in the undergraduate exam papers of Cambridge University, that bastion of Anglican respectability.

Conversely, other scientists opposed the theory on scientific grounds alone or on religious grounds alone, or sometimes on both. There were scientific popularisers and clerics who readily accepted Darwin's theory and quickly adapted it into their doctrine of creation. And there were some clerics, a minority as it happens, who opposed the theory strongly, thinking, like the creationists of today, that it would undermine Christian morality and notions of human value.

Darwin himself had many clerical friends, and out of his 2,000 correspondents, around 200 were clergymen, some of whom provided him with biological information for his publications. After Darwin had sent an advance copy of *The Origin* to the novelist and socialist Revd Charles Kingsley, who in 1860 became professor of modern history at Cambridge, Kingsley wrote back with a delighted response saying that, "All I have seen of it awes me." He went on to comment that it is:

> Just as noble a conception of Deity, to believe that He created primal forms capable of self-development...as to believe that He required a fresh act of intervention to supply the lacunas [gaps] which He Himself had made.[1]

Darwin was so impressed with this response that he quoted these lines in the second edition of *The Origin*. It is interesting to note that the earliest written theological response to Darwin's book in existence, penned six days *before* its official publication day, was such a positive one.

the Oxford debate of 1860

The following year a debate took place in Oxford between the Bishop of Oxford, "Soapy Sam" Wilberforce, and the person later dubbed "Darwin's bull-dog", Thomas Huxley. In the late 19th and early 20th centuries, the debate attained iconic status in the so-called "warfare literature" between science and religion. Subsequently, however, historians have reassessed the event and its context, and provided a more balanced account of what actually happened.[2]

The occasion was the annual meeting of the British Association for the Advancement of Science, the main venue in that era for the presentation and discussion of the latest science. Cleric-scientists had dominated the advances in science in Britain during the first half of the 19th century. No less than forty-one Anglican clergymen had presided over the various sections of the British Association during the period 1831-1865, and Bishop Wilberforce himself had been a Vice-President.

It was, therefore, entirely natural that Wilberforce should be called to assess Darwin's theory, published only seven months earlier. Wilberforce used his talk to summarise the scientific points, emphasising that, "we have no sympathy with those who object to any facts or alleged facts in nature, or to any inference logically deduced from them, because they believe them to contradict what it appears to them is taught by Revelation."[3]

This was no science vs. religion debate, but a well-informed critique of Darwin's new theory. "I have just read the 'Quarterly' [in which Wilberforce's criticism was published]," Darwin later wrote to his friend, the botanist Joseph Hooker, in July 1860. "It is uncommonly clever; it picks out with skill all the most conjectural parts, and brings forward well all the difficulties."[4]

Because Darwin was ill and unable to attend the Oxford meeting, Huxley rose to respond to Wilberforce's talk. According to Hooker, however, Huxley's voice could not be heard in the packed hall, and it was Hooker himself who then gave a triumphant defence of natural selection. Whatever the exact truth of what happened – and there are several conflicting accounts – it is clear that an important debate took place. The contemporary description, published in *The Athenaeum*, probably reflects the occasion best, reporting that Huxley and the other speakers had each "found foemen worthy of their steel, and have made their charges and countercharges very much to their own satisfaction and the delight of their respective friends."[5]

Somewhat surprisingly, an early convert to evolution, the naturalist Henry Baker Tristram, was so persuaded by Wilberforce's scientific arguments, that he was *de-converted* as a result of his Oxford speech. The occasion was clearly far from a complete triumph for Darwinism.

Wilberforce was not typical of the Anglican Church leaders of the time in his opposition to evolution. Of greater significance was the fact that the future Archbishop of Canterbury, Frederick Temple, gave the official sermon at the same Oxford meeting, arguing that the activity of God was to be discerned throughout the laws governing the natural world, not in the gaps in current scientific knowledge. Although Temple did not mention Darwin by name, one member of his congregation recounted afterwards that "he espoused Darwin's ideas fully."[6] Later Temple was to develop this theme in his Bampton lectures of 1884, in which he presented a specifically Darwinian view of evolution.[7]

Similar points were made by Aubrey Moore, a Fellow of St. John's College, Oxford, and Curator of the Oxford Botanical Gardens. Moore maintained that Darwinism had done the Church a great service in helping it rid itself of the more extreme forms of natural theology. He claimed that there was a special affinity between Darwinism and Christian theology, remarking that "Darwinism appeared, and, under the guise of a foe, did the work of a friend".[8]

The reason for this affinity, claimed Moore, was based on the intimate involvement of God in his creation as revealed in Christian theology. Moore argued:

> There are not, and cannot be, any Divine interpositions in nature, for God cannot interfere with Himself. His creative activity is present everywhere. There is no division of labour between God and nature, or God and law…For the Christian theologian the facts of nature are the acts of God.[9]

Ironically Huxley himself, whilst a passionate defender of evolution as "common descent with modification", never accepted Darwin's proposed mechanism of natural selection. Huxley was wary of giving too much place for "chance" in the process because that seemed to him to open the way for supernatural intervention. The fact that today's creationists worry about "chance" for precisely the opposite reason gives an indication of how complex reactions to evolution can be. Huxley himself thought that evolution represented the inexorable working out of natural laws, "a wider teleology which is not touched by the doctrine of Evolution" that "does not even come into contact with Theism, considered as a philosophical doctrine."[10]

Huxley's use of evolution as a battering-ram to attack the late-Victorian established Church had little to do with any inherent conflict between science and religion and rather more to do with the emerging professional class of scientists during this period, and their desire to wrest for themselves the financial resources and intellectual prestige in society that remained the prerogative of the Church. But when it came to Huxley's own views about the role of natural law in evolution, it is easy to see how congenial his position was to an understanding of God as law-giver who created through process rather than by divine fiat.

the reception of evolution in North America

Considering the present American antipathy to the theory, it is ironic that evolution was popularised in North America largely by Christian academics. Foremost among these was Asa Gray, Professor of Natural History at Harvard and a committed Christian. He was Darwin's long-term correspondent and confidante who helped organise the publication of *The Origin* in America and who had debated the question of evolution and design with Darwin over many years.

Other Christian thinkers were equally supportive. James McCosh was president of the College of New Jersey (later to become Princeton University). Firmly rooted in the Calvinist tradition, McCosh held strongly to the concept of natural selection, but

Evolution was popularised in North America largely by Christian academics.

equally strongly to the belief that "the natural origin of species is not inconsistent with intelligent design in nature or with the existence of a personal Creator of the world".[11]

George Wright was a theologian and geologist, whose books on glacial geology were for years the standard texts on the subject. He was not only a vigorous proponent of Darwinism but believed, as the historian James Moore has pointed out, "that Darwin's work actually allies itself with the Reformed faith in discouraging romantic, sentimental, and optimistic interpretations of nature."[12]

Alexander Winchell was professor of geology and paleontology at the University of Michigan, and a leading Methodist spokesman. He played a major role in organising geology as a science in the United States and was a founding member of the American Geological Society, coming progressively closer to a Darwinian understanding of evolution during the course of his career.

James Dana was professor of Natural History at Yale and editor of *The American Journal of Science*. He was another American geologist of orthodox Christian conviction who accepted Darwinian evolution after some initial doubts, initiating an influential series of lectures on evolution at Yale in 1883. As he commented, "it is not atheism to believe in a development theory, if it be admitted at the same time that Nature exists by the will and continued act of God".[13]

Through the work of eminent scientists such as Gray, McCosh, Wright, Winchell, and Dana – scientists who were also serious and committed Christians – Darwinian evolution spread rapidly within US academia and beyond. Indeed, it spread so rapidly that, according to the American historian George

Virtually every American Protestant zoologist and botanist accepted some form of evolution by the early 1870s.

Marsden, "with the exception of Harvard's Louis Agassiz, virtually every American Protestant zoologist and botanist accepted some form of evolution by the early 1870s."[14] In the words of the British historian James Moore, author of the definitive book tracing the reception of Darwinism in Britain and America in the 19th century, "with but few exceptions the leading Christian thinkers in Great Britain and America came to terms quite readily with Darwinism and evolution."[15]

Darwinism in the twentieth century

The discovery of genes and the re-discovery of the laws of inheritance, originally published in 1866 by Gregor Mendel, the Abbot of a Moravian Augustinian monastery, gave Darwinian evolution a further boost in the early decades of the 20th century. It was the fusion of population genetics with natural selection that led to the so-called "neo-Darwinian synthesis" that remains today's orthodoxy.

Once again, far from being unremittingly hostile or antagonistic towards the evolving science, several of the key players, indeed founders, of neo-Darwinism were committed Christians. Theodosius Dobzhansky, best remembered for his aphorism that "nothing in biology makes sense except in the light of evolution," was an Orthodox Christian. The statistician RA Fisher, who brought mathematical rigour to population genetics and has been described by Richard Dawkins as "the greatest of [Darwin's] successors", was a committed Anglican.[16] The ornithologist David Lack, picked by Thomas Huxley's grandson, Julian, to research Darwin's finches on the Galapagos Islands, converted to Christian faith from agnosticism in the very year that he published his famous book *Darwin's Finches*.

Given the relatively rapid recognition of Darwinian evolution among Christian thinkers in the US and UK, not to mention the significant role in the theory's reception and development played by a number of Christian scientists, it may seem surprising that the popular reception was rather more muted. This was not so much because the general public found it difficult to grasp the idea (although that probably played a part) as because they often first encountered evolution not as a biological theory but through the distorting lens of a particular ideology.

This was particularly so in the writings of the philosopher Herbert Spencer, which were hugely influential in America. Spencer maintained that the entire universe was ascending towards ultimate perfection through the operation of inexorable physical laws for the "evolution" of social structures. Darwin himself found these views highly questionable, remarking of Spencer's "fundamental generalisations" that "they do not seem to me to be of any strictly scientific use".[16]

More ominously, Spencer, who coined the phrase "survival of the fittest", saw in evolution a "stern discipline" which had, for the good of society, to be pursued. He campaigned vigorously against all state attempts to ameliorate human suffering, criticising the "spurious philanthropists who, to prevent present misery, would entail greater misery on future generations."

Blind to the fact that under the natural order of things society is constantly excreting its unhealthy, imbecile, slow, vacillating, faithless members, these unthinking, though well-meaning, men advocate an interference which not only stops the purifying process, but even increases the vitiation…encouraging the multiplication of the reckless and incompetent by offering them an unfailing provision.[18]

> *From the earliest times, evolution was understood - and sometimes rejected - as a philosophical, social or political theory, rather than simply a biological one.*

When the general public encountered Darwinian evolution through such a brutal social doctrine, it is little surprise that many, in particular many of the poorest and most socially disadvantaged, rejected it.

Social Darwinism did not have the monopoly on interpreting evolution. Indeed, in its time evolution has been used in support of every "ism" imaginable, including socialism, capitalism, racism, eugenics, feminism, theism and atheism. As George Bernard Shaw once remarked, Darwin "had the luck to please everybody who had an axe to grind".[19] The key point is that, from the earliest times, evolution was understood – and sometimes *rejected* – as a philosophical, social or political theory, rather than simply a biological one.

fundamentalism and Darwin

Today, it is assumed that a Christian "fundamentalist" must be "anti-Darwinian". It is, therefore, intriguing to learn that many of the early "fundamentalists" actually held to evolution, providing it was seen simply as the way that God had chosen to bring biological diversity into being by a long process.

This is well illustrated by the publication, from which the word "fundamentalism" is partially derived, of a mass-produced series of essays in twelve volumes known as *The Fundamentals*, written by conservative Protestants in the period 1910–15. The aim of *The Fundamentals* was to counteract the liberal theology that was then flooding into American churches from Germany. Among these essays there were a number by evangelical writers committed to evolution, such as Benjamin Warfield, who called himself a "Darwinian of the purest water", James Orr, who pointed out that Genesis was not written as a scientific text, and the geologist George Wright.

> *Many of the early "fundamentalists" actually held to evolution.*

Orr wrote that "'Evolution'…is coming to be recognised as but a new name for "creation," only that the creative power now works from within." True, *The Fundamentals* also contained essays opposed to evolution, such as Dyson Hague's, but that is just the point: the early "fundamentalists" allowed a diversity of views within their midst on such topics.

the twentieth century and the rise of creationism

Creationism is largely a 20th century phenomenon and its historical roots have been helpfully surveyed by the historian Ronald Numbers.[20] Its impetus came from several directions, not least the fear, widespread in the US, that the doctrine of "might is right", which fuelled German expansionism during the First World War, was being justified by Darwinian ideology.

If that kind of ideology became dominant in the US, reasoned William Jennings Bryan, liberal reformer and thrice-failed Democrat contender for the Presidency, then the struggle for the rights of the poor and oppressed would be undermined. His "creationism" had little to do with biology but rather was a reaction against "the merciless law by which the strong crowd out and kill off the weak".[21]

Bryan led a vigorous anti-evolution crusade in the early 1920s, fuelled by the spread of compulsory state-supported secondary-school education that culminated in the infamous Scopes Trial of 1925. The trial, which quickly became a media circus, was a challenge to a newly-passed bill by the state of Tennessee banning the teaching of evolution in schools. Bryan died a week after it ended, a martyr to the cause, and the creationist movement temporarily ran out of steam.

It was not until the early 1960s that creationism was revived in the US, this time by the publication of a book called *The Genesis Flood*, written by a lecturer in civil engineering, Henry Morris, and a theologian, John Whitcomb. Within a quarter of a century *The Genesis Flood* had gone through twenty-nine printings and sold over 200,000 copies, helping to found several creationist societies that remain active to the present day.

The 1920s creationist movement had been anti-Darwinian without propounding a young earth, but the 1960s version went for an earth less than 10,000 years old and creation in six literal 24-hour days. Not since the 18th century had people widely held such beliefs.

The new Young Earth Creationism (YEC) was, paradoxically, both anti-science and, at the same, time deeply influenced by modernism, the belief that science provides the only acceptable framework for reliable knowledge. YEC proponents started looking to the early chapters of Genesis as if they represented scientific texts, thereby discarding many centuries of Biblical interpretation. It was no accident that YEC supporters were often engineers and material scientists, looking to the Bible as a manual in support of "scientific creationism", as if theology somehow became more reliable by attaching the adjective "scientific".

conclusion

Darwinian evolution was accepted by Christians from the earliest days following the publication of *The Origin of Species*. In a comparatively short period of time it was readily accommodated by leading Christian thinkers, although, partly because they encountered it as a social or philosophical system, it never found quite as positive a reception among the general public.

The phenomenon of "scientific creationism" with which we are familiar today is a peculiarly modern one. Because of its rapid growth in mid-to-late 20th century America, many outside the Church gained the impression that Christians were generally anti-Darwinian – despite the fact that mainstream denominations on both sides of the Atlantic continued the tradition of teaching evolution in their schools and colleges and that evolution continued to be understood by theologians simply as God's method for bringing biological diversity into being.

The fact remains, however, that creationism and, latterly, Intelligent Design, have made significant inroads into European as well as US public awareness over recent decades. The true extent of those inroads is explored in the next chapter.

chapter 2 - references

1. Charles Kingsley to Charles Darwin, 18 November 1859.

2. See, for example, John Hedley Brooke, "The Wilberforce-Huxley Debate: Why Did It Happen?", in *Science and Christian Belief*, 2001, Volume 13, pp. 127-41.

3. *The Quarterly Review*, cviii, July 1860, pp. 225-64; reprinted in Samuel Wilberforce, *Essays contributed to the Quarterly Review* (London, 1874), p. 256.

4. Letter to Joseph Hooker, 20(?) July 1860.

5. *The Athenaeum*, 7 July 1860, p. 19, col. i.

6. Denis Alexander, *Rebuilding the Matrix – Science and Faith in the 21st Century* (Oxford: Lion, 2001), p. 196.

7. Frederick Temple, *The Relations Between Religion and Science* (Macmillan, 1885).

8. Aubrey Moore, "The Christian Doctrine of God", in Charles Gore, ed., *Lux Mundi* (Murray, 1891; 12th edn), p. 73.

9. Alexander, *Rebuilding the Matrix*, p. 177.

10. Brooke, "The Wilberforce-Huxley Debate", p. 140.

11. Alexander, *Rebuilding the Matrix*, pp. 200-201.

12. Alexander, *Rebuilding the Matrix*, p. 194.

13. Alexander, *Rebuilding the Matrix*, p. 194.

14. GM Marsden in *Science and Creationism* A Montagu, ed., (Oxford University Press, 1984), p. 101.

15. JR Moore, *The Post-Darwinian Controversies*, (Cambridge University Press, 1979), p. 92.

16. Dawkins, *Blind Watchmaker*, p. 199.

17. Darwin, *Autobiography*, p. 109.

18. Herbert Spencer, *Social Statics* (John Chapman, 1851). Spencer was, in fact, basing his ideas on Lamarckian rather than Darwinian evolution at this stage, but he seized on and championed natural selection when he encountered it a decade later.

19. Alexander, *Rebuilding the Matrix*, p. 207.

20. RL Numbers in *The Creationists* (Boston: Harvard University Press, 2006; 2nd edn).

21. Cited in EJ Larson, *Evolution – the Remarkable History of a Scientific Theory* (Modern Library, 2006), p. 207.

Darwin today

research in the USA

America is renowned as the most anti-Darwinian country in the West. A 2005 survey, and other surveys since, revealed that in this most scientifically and technologically advanced country, 42% of the population adopt the creationist position in agreeing that humans and other living things have existed in their present form since the beginning of time, a percentage increasing to 70% amongst white evangelicals. In contrast to this, 48% of Americans believe in evolution, around a third of whom believe in evolution "guided by a supreme being."[1]

Inevitably, there are complexities and ambiguities within such results. For example, in one US study, while 78% of adults accept the evolution of plants and animals, 62% said they believed God had created humans as whole persons without any evolutionary development.[2] Many people seem unworried by evolution in general, but draw the line at human evolution, believing that this challenges notions of human value and identity.

The percentage of Americans opposed to evolution seems to have remained stable over recent decades. Since 1982, Gallup polls have been reporting the percentage of Americans who agree with the statement that "God created human beings pretty much in their present form at one time within the last 10,000 years or so." From a figure of 42% in 1982, the percentages have oscillated between 43% and 47% ever since, with 44% recorded for 2008.[3] Presidents come and go. The economy waxes and wanes. Atheists and creationists keep the publishers busy. And America continues to pioneer great biological projects, such as the sequencing of the human genome (a project led by a Christian evolutionary biologist, Francis Collins). But through it all, nearly half the US population maintains its anti-Darwinian beliefs.

Nearly half the US population maintains anti-Darwinian beliefs.

The US creationist figures are strikingly high when compared with most European countries, where the level of acceptance of Darwinian evolution is typically in the range 60-80%. Only in Turkey are the levels of creationist belief higher than in the US.[4]

The American antipathy to evolution appears to be linked closely with the struggle over who decides what should be taught in US schools. Following the 1925 Scopes Trial, publishers eliminated most material about evolution from biology textbooks. In 1942, a nationwide survey of high school biology teachers indicated that fewer than 50% were teaching anything about organic evolution in their science courses.[5] In January 1961, a bill to repeal Tennessee's so-called "monkey laws", still in force 30 years after the Scopes trial, was passionately opposed by people who argued that evolution "drives God out of the universe" and "leads to communism".[6] Data from the late 1980s suggested that 25-30% of US high school biology teachers believed in "special creation" at that time.[7] Today, 41% of Americans still think that parents, not scientists or teachers, should have the final say as to whether and how evolution is taught in schools.[8]

> Today, 41% of Americans still think that parents, not scientists or teachers, should have the final say as to whether and how evolution is taught in schools.

Over recent years, it is Intelligent Design (ID) that has been attracting attention in the US. ID is distinct from creationism, as discussed below, and it is harder for polling organisations to obtain an accurate assessment of its level of acceptance, mainly due to confusion about the meaning of the term.[9] It therefore seems likely that polling questions on creationism in fact harvest replies from ID supporters.

Whatever the exact figures, there is little doubt that the US remains the international powerhouse for the generation of creationist and ID support, exported round the world by creationist organisations, magazines and websites. There are particular religious and cultural reasons why this should be so, such as the popularity of fundamentalist Christianity, sensitivities about state control of public education, and the perception of evolution as anti-religious philosophy rather than science. The situation in the UK has been somewhat different – at least historically.

research in the UK

Young Earth Creationism and Intelligent Design may be relatively recent phenomena in the US, but they are even more recent in the UK. For this reason there are very few studies describing the extent and nature of non-evolutionary beliefs in the UK, and no longitudinal data to track the long-term growth or decline of such beliefs.

According to an Ipsos/MORI poll conducted for the BBC in January 2006, 48% of people believe in the "evolution theory", which was defined in the survey as "human kind [having] developed over millions of years from less advanced forms of life. God had no part in this process."[11]

The same survey reported that 22% believed in the "creationism theory" ("that God created human kind pretty much in his/her present form at one time within the last 10,000 years") and 17% in the "intelligent design theory" ("that certain features of living things are best explained by the intervention of a supernatural being, e.g. God"). In July the same year, OpinionPanel asked university students the same questions, with similar results: 56% favoured evolution, 12% creationism, and 19% intelligent design.[11]

Such data are valuable but suffer from the problem that they force respondents into distinct, pre-existing categories, compartmentalised into misleading "either-or" dichotomies. Single questions with only a, b or c options to choose from are unlikely to capture the complexity of the full situation.

For this reason, Theos commissioned the polling company ComRes to conduct an extensive survey into the true extent and nature of evolutionary and non-evolutionary beliefs in the UK, among 2,000 adults.[12] This survey asked people their opinions of creationism, Intelligent Design, and evolution from a number of different angles, sometimes naming the positions, sometimes not, as well as separately asking about people's religious beliefs, behaviour, and affiliation. By doing this, the data could be analysed in such a way as to measure accurately the true state of beliefs in the UK.

The results were complex, bearing out the hypothesis that people's opinions in this matter are not necessarily well-formed or coherent. Many people simply have not thought in any depth about Darwinian evolution, still less Intelligent Design and, accordingly, they articulate opinions that appear to be inconsistent or ill-thought-through. Such confusion and complexity acknowledged, however, clear patterns emerged.

young earth creationism

17% of people agreed with the statement that "humans were created by God some time within the last 10,000 years".

The study found that 17% of people agreed with the statement that "humans were created by God some time within the last 10,000 years", a statement consistent with the Young Earth Creation (YEC) position, although one that could also include old earth creationism.

When respondents were subsequently presented with an explicit definition of Young Earth Creationism ("the idea that God created the world sometime in the last 10,000 years"), 11% said they thought this was "definitely true" and 21% "probably true", suggesting that the YEC group, like any other, comprises a smaller number of convinced adherents and a larger fringe who are less secure in their convictions.

These two results were supported by people's attitude to the status of Darwinian evolution as a theory. Respondents were told that "Darwinian evolution is the idea that life today, including human life, developed over millions of years from earlier species, by a process of natural selection," and were asked what they thought of this. About a tenth (9%) of respondents said, "it is a theory which has been disproved by the evidence," with a further tenth (10%) saying "it is a theory with very little evidence to support it."

Altogether, these results suggest that around one in ten people in the UK would qualify as convinced Young Earth Creationists, with perhaps as many again being inclined towards that view.

intelligent design

Respondents were asked about Intelligent Design (ID), a more problematic subject, given the relative novelty and complexity of this idea (certainly in comparison to Young Earth Creationism). Just over one in ten (11%) of the sample agreed with the statement, "humans evolved by a process of evolution which required the special intervention of God or a higher power at key stages."[13]

> *Just over one in ten (11%) of the sample agreed with the statement, "humans evolved by a process of evolution which required the special intervention of God or a higher power at key stages."*

There was, perhaps understandably, some tension between this result and that from a subsequent question which specifically mentioned Intelligent Design. Respondents were explicitly presented with a definition of ID ("the idea that evolution alone is not enough to explain the complex structures of some living things, so the intervention of a designer is needed at key stages") and asked whether they thought it was definitely/probably un/true. Around one in seven people (14%) said they thought it was "definitely true," but a surprising 37% said they thought it was "probably true."

This comparably high figure receives some confirmation from the fact that 36% of respondents said that they thought Darwinian evolution "is a theory that is still waiting to be proved or disproved." Taken together, these two sets of data appear to suggest that although around one in seven of the population would qualify as a confirmed "IDer", a rather higher proportion – perhaps as high as one in three – is sufficiently uncertain about Darwinian evolution to wish to "hedge their bets" and cite some form of designer intervention as a way of joining all the dots.

evolution

In contrast to this, around two thirds of the sample could be described as "believing in evolution". Just over a third of respondents (37%) agreed that "humans evolved by a process of evolution which removes any need for God", and just under a third (28%) that "humans evolved by a process of evolution which can be seen as part of God's plan."

These figures broadly concur with the results from the questions which explicitly presented respondents with the concepts of theistic and atheistic evolution. When presented with a definition of theistic evolution ("the idea that evolution is the means that God used for the creation of all living things on earth") 12% of people said they thought it was definitely true and 32% said it was probably true. By contrast when presented with a definition of atheistic evolution ("the idea that evolution makes belief in God unnecessary and absurd") 13% of people said they thought it was definitely true and 21% said it was probably true.

Just over a third of respondents (37%) agreed that "humans evolved by a process of evolution which removes any need for God".

Thus, with evolution, as with Young Earth Creationism and Intelligent Design, a larger fringe of "probablys" surrounds a smaller core of "definites". While a proportion – perhaps 25% - is confident in its evolutionary convictions, a greater proportion appears to be unsure and is inclined to hedge its bets.

When presented with a definition of theistic evolution 12% of people said they thought it was definitely true and 32% said it was probably true.

conclusion

Overall, the results from the Theos/ComRes study underline how difficult it is to say with absolute precision and confidence that the population divides into x, y and z% of evolutionists, IDers or creationists. Many people are too unclear about the options and uncertain of their own beliefs to come out definitively as one or another.

What the data do reveal is that in the UK around one in ten people are convinced Young Earth Creationists, about one in seven hold to some form of ID, and one in four are confident evolutionists. The remaining half of the population is rather less certain, generally favouring evolution over other theories, but insufficiently confident of its merits, and therefore inclined to temper their conviction with other explanations.

Either way, it appears that, in the country of Darwin's birth, a century and a half after the publication of his masterwork, only about one in four people would qualify as confirmed Darwinians, with at least as many being actively hostile towards Darwinian evolution, and an even larger portion being inclined towards Darwinism but distinctly unsure about its merits. The reasons for this are explored in the next chapter.

chapter 3 - references

1. The Pew Forum Surveys, 30 August 2005. See: http://pewforum.org/docs/?DocID=115#3.

2. JD Miller, EC Scott and S Okamoto, "Public acceptance of evolution" in *Science* 313 (2006) pp. 765-766.

3. http://www.gallup.com/poll/21814/Evolution-Creationism-Intelligent-Design.aspx.

4. Miller et al., "Public acceptance".

5. D Nelkin, *The Creation Controversy* (WW Norton, 1982), p. 33.

6. W Dykeman & J Stokeley, "Scopes and Evolution - the Jury is Still Out", in *New York Times Magazine*, 12 March 1971, pp. 72-76.

7. RA Eve and FB Harrold, *The Creationist Movement in Modern America* (Twayne Publishers, 1991), p. 188.

8. http://pewforum.org/docs/?DocID=115.

9. http://people-press.org/commentary/?analysisid=118.

10. Ipsos/MORI, "BBC Survey On The Origins Of Life", http://www.ipsos-mori.com/content/bbc-survey-on-the-origins-of-life.ashx.

11. Harriet Swain, "How did we get here?" *The Guardian*, 15 August 2006.

12. The results of this are published in a separate report in the *Rescuing Darwin* series.

13. This is about as close as you can get to defining the ID position in 20 or so words, although it is possible that some pro-Darwinian theistic evolutionists might also locate themselves in this group.

Darwin in the crossfire

If around a quarter of the British population are committed in their adherence to Young Earth Creationism or Intelligent Design, and at least as many again are uncertain in their attitude towards evolution, that translates into around 20 million adults who are more or less ill-disposed towards Darwinian evolution. So long after the theory's publication and in the context of near-universal scientific agreement on the basic tenets of the theory, that is an extraordinarily high number.

> *Around 20 million adults are more or less ill-disposed towards Darwinian evolution.*

Given the size of this group, it would be naïve to expect a single, simple reason for their rejection of evolution. Indeed, one of the core messages of *Doubting Darwin*, a qualitative research study of leading proponents of Young Earth Creationism and Intelligent Design in the UK, commissioned by Theos and conducted by the social ethnographic research company ESRO, is that there is considerably greater complexity within these positions than is usually recognised. Young Earth Creationists and Intelligent Design proponents may reject evolution (and even then they do so to varying degrees) but they are far from united over why they do so or what stands in its place.

Such diversity recognised, however, it is clear that the overarching conviction – and one that is paradoxically shared by "Darwinian fundamentalists" – is that somehow evolution by natural selection is incompatible with belief in God. In spite of what Darwin himself thought, evolution is deemed by many to be essentially atheistic.

One does not need to travel very far to discover why this is so. Those most eager to defend Darwin today are often those who write most derisively about religion. Faith, they say, "means blind trust…even in the teeth of experience." [1] It is "a kind of mental illness", [2] "a mental virus…[with] its accompanying gang of secondary infections", [3] "one of the world's great evils, comparable to the smallpox virus but harder to eradicate". [4]

In all fairness, it is sometimes difficult to know exactly what is meant by these seemingly malicious sentiments, as there is a disconcerting slipperiness about their rhetoric. When criticised for his use of the word "robot" to describe human beings in *The Selfish Gene*,

Richard Dawkins replied, "Part of the problem lies with the popular, but erroneous, associations of the word 'robot'", before going on to tell people what they should understand from the word.[5] Similarly, when taken to task by the philosopher Mary Midgley for his careless use of the word "selfish" to describe genes, Dawkins replied, "In effect I am saying: 'Provided I define selfishness in a particular way an oak tree, or a gene, may legitimately be described as selfish.'"[6]

This is peculiarly reminiscent of Humpty Dumpty in Lewis Carroll's *Through the looking glass* – "'When I use a word,' Humpty Dumpty said in rather a scornful tone, 'it means just what I choose it to mean – neither more nor less.'" – and it makes pinning down what is actually meant rather difficult.

Nevertheless, whether the use of the word "virus" to describe faith is intended to be somehow technical or "special",[7] thereby neutralising its more obvious associations (such as its use to describe the Jewish faith in the 1930s), it is clear that there is considerable hostility, even spite, in the word. When Darwin's most prominent modern disciples, in contrast to their master, so openly and witheringly revile religious belief, is it any wonder that religious believers become ill-disposed towards Darwinism?

The precise reasons for that hostility and for the conviction that Darwinism is necessarily atheistic appear to be rooted in the idea that "religion is a scientific theory",[8] "a competing explanation for facts about the universe and life".[9] More specifically, it is an alternative to natural selection. "God and natural selection are…the only two workable theories we have of why we exist."[10]

This is bizarrely similar to the view of Young Earth Creationists who take the early chapters of Genesis to be a literal and scientifically-accurate account of creation, but is thoroughly dismissed by serious theologians and philosophers. It is "a kind of category mistake", as Rowan Williams has called it, treating "the Bible [as if it] were a theory like other theories":

It's not as if the writer of Genesis…sat down and said well, how am I going to explain all this…I know "In the beginning God created the heavens and the earth."[11]

Quite why this erroneous understanding of Genesis as a kind of proto-scientific textbook, and religion as a (peculiarly-constructed) scientific theory, persists, in the teeth of on-going biblical studies and theological reflection, is far from clear. However, its impact is ultimately to foster conflict where there is none, and to turn those who might otherwise be disposed towards Darwinian evolution away from the theory.

a bleak vision

Whilst this is the most obvious reason for the widespread rejection of Darwinism, it is not the only one. It will be noted that 25%, the percentage of adults who actively reject evolution, is far above the percentage of committed religious believers in the UK, let alone the percentage of religious believers who are anti-evolution (a significant proportion of practising Christians – 60% – believe that theistic evolution is either probably or definitely true). The reason for Darwin's rejection extends beyond (some of) his disciples' contempt for religion.

> *Darwinian evolution has become associated with a massively reductive agenda, a kind of systematic "nothing-buttery".*

Although it is more difficult to identify precisely what this might be, it seems to be linked with the way in which, over recent years, Darwinian evolution has become associated with a massively reductive agenda, a kind of systematic "nothing-buttery". [12]

Although some, Richard Dawkins among them, claim that "'reductionism' is one of those things, like sin, that is only mentioned by people who are against it", [13] other Darwinians are more honest about their intent. "Darwin's dangerous idea is reductionism incarnate," according to Daniel Dennett. [14]

Thus, according to this modern reading of evolution by natural selection, human beings are "robot[s]", [15] "survival machines…blindly programmed to preserve the[ir]…genes". [16] The "individual organism [is] not fundamental to life [but]…a secondary, derived phenomenon", [17] "only the vehicle (of genes), part of an elaborate device to preserve and spread them with the least possible biochemical perturbation". [18]

Consequently, everything we might think of as distinctively human is demolished. Morality (in as far as we can still talk about it) becomes calculating and fundamentally self-interested, ethical systems arbitrary, agency an illusion, and human beings completely irrelevant and accidental. The human mind is dismantled, becoming "an artefact created when memes restructure a human brain so as to make it a better habitat for memes". [19] The universe is reduced to "blind forces and physical replication" with "no purpose, no evil and no good, nothing but blind, pitiless indifference". [20] And love, charity, compassion, and altruism are "tendencies…grounded in underlying selfishness". [21] The end result is not appealing:

> No hint of genuine charity ameliorates our vision of society, once sentimentalism has been laid aside. What passes for co-operation turns out to be

a mixture of opportunism and exploitation … Where it is in his interest, every organism may reasonably be expected to aid his fellows. Where he has no alternative, he submits to the yoke of communal servitude. Yet given a full chance to act in his own interest, nothing but expedience will restrain him from brutalising, from maiming, from murdering – his brother, his mate, his parent, or his child. Scratch an 'altruist' and watch a 'hypocrite' bleed.[22]

Given that Darwinian evolution has become bound up with such bleak visions over recent years – bleak and *highly contested* visions: many Darwinian evolutionists protest that such ideas owe rather more to imagination than to evidence[23] – it is perhaps not surprising that people should turn away from it. In much the same way as earlier generations encountered evolution through a particularly ugly form of Social Darwinism, and not surprisingly then rejected it, many today, it seems, associate it with an amoral, materialist, hopeless, selfish outlook on life, which they are extremely reluctant to countersign and which turns them firmly against the theory.

It is precisely this conception of Darwinian evolution that lies at the root of the peculiarly modern phenomenon of Intelligent Design.

Intelligent Design

The modern Intelligent Design movement was triggered by University of California law professor, Phillip E Johnson. Johnson recounts how he was on sabbatical at University College, London in 1987, when he came across Richard Dawkins' book *The Blind Watchmaker*.[24] It was Dawkins' assertions about evolution as a godless process, together with what Johnson perceived as its lack of evidence that spurred him into his anti-Darwinian crusade. That Dawkins' work should have been the trigger for the ID movement is somewhat ironic.

> *That Dawkins' work should have been the trigger for the ID movement is somewhat ironic.*

A central target for Johnson's attacks was the "naturalism" that he saw pervading science in general and evolution in particular. Impressed by Dawkins, Johnson saw evolution as "a materialistic process in which God played no part", writing that "'evolution' in the Darwinian sense is by definition mindless and godless".[25] Theistic evolutionists, who saw evolution as a description of the creative process whereby God brings about biological diversity, were given short shrift by Johnson who described the idea of evolution as a "God-guided system of gradual creation" as a "mistake".[26]

the historical background to design arguments

The term "Intelligent Design" is a slippery one and is often confused with the traditional "arguments from design" that have a long history, going back to the ancient Stoic philosophers and popularised by the Roman lawyer Cicero in his book *The Nature of the Gods*, before being taken up by early Christian thinkers, such as Tertullian, as a way of promoting belief in God.

The idea of design in the world was deployed to great effect by many of the founders of modern science in the 17th century, playing a central role in what came to be known as "natural theology". For some, this was the attempt to derive the existence and even (something about) the character of God from the properties of the natural world. For others, it was more a way of appreciating the work in creation of a God already known by revelation. Robert Boyle, a committed Christian and one of the early founders of the Royal Society, viewed the world as a complex machine:

> Like a rare clock…where all things are so skillfully contrived, that the engine being once set a-moving, all things proceed, according to the artificer's first design…by virtue of the general and primitive contrivance of the whole engine.[27]

God's activity in nature, Boyle and others thought, was continuous and complete. There were no "gaps" that could be attributed to forces or agents outside of God's immediate control. Nature was not autonomous. The business of science was to describe God's handiwork to the best of human ability.

This helps to explain why the early Royal Society made a specific decision not to include religious discussions within their proceedings. For sure, this was to avoid entanglement with the tortured religious politics of mid-17th century Britain, but it also reflected the conviction that the role of the new "mechanical philosophy", as science was often then called, was to exclude teleology, the question of ultimate goals, and stick to the secondary causes that the primary cause, God, had used to bring about his creation.

the contemporary ID movement

The anti-Darwinian ID movement, spearheaded by Johnson in the early 1990s had a very different agenda from the promotion of the general idea of "design". Indeed, the word "design" has multiple meanings, which bedevil debates in this area.

All theists believe in "design" in the sense that they believe in a God who has intentions and purposes for the universe. They also believe that God has "designed" the properties of the universe (by fine-tuning the physical constants that underwrite the universe, for example) to facilitate the existence of intelligent life. Whether God designs one universe or many is irrelevant to the conviction that God has intentions for this particular one. This is not, however, the kind of design that ID proponents tend to highlight. Instead, they wish to demonstrate the existence of design, and by inference a designer, based upon the properties of specific, complex biological systems. In this regard, ID is not the same as creationism, as ID proponents specifically reject appeals to religious texts as a source for their beliefs, and aim to present ID as a *scientific* alternative, which should be taught alongside evolution in science lessons.

ID proponents are quite varied in their own religious beliefs and in the extent to which they accept evolutionary theory. For example, the Catholic biochemist Michael Behe admits the common ancestry of humans with the apes, the Presbyterian Johnson does not, and the mathematician and philosopher William Dembski, now teaching at the Southwestern Baptist Theological Seminary, prevaricates. There are also atheists and agnostics amongst ID proponents, while Jonathan Wells, a Fellow of The Discovery Institute in Seattle, was trained as a minister in the Unification Church founded by Sun Myung Moon.

What does unite ID proponents is a shared antipathy to Darwinian evolution as an inference to the best explanation for the origins of biological diversity, including the origins of all biological complex systems. Dembski is explicit in stating that the one point that ID supporters share in common with "scientific creationists" is that "mutations and natural selection are insufficient to bring about the development of all living kinds from a single organism."[28]

> *ID is not the same as creationism, as ID proponents specifically reject appeals to religious texts as a source for their beliefs.*

ID proponents propose that biological entities, such as the bacterial flagellum, a complex molecular "outboard motor" with which bacteria swim around, are "irreducibly complex", meaning that they are only functional if all components are present. Since Darwinian evolution requires small, incremental changes such entities could not, they argue, have evolved. Such irreducibly complex entities are explained by a "design inference", meaning that such entities in nature can be identified as displaying design. The "design language" in use here is that of the architect or engineer who precisely specifies the organisation of the end-product.

ID proponents claim that their ideas are strictly scientific, not religious, and should, therefore, be taught in science lessons as an alternative view to evolution. This has led to American court cases about the teaching of ID in schools, such as the recent Dover Trial in which a public school board in the US was taken to court for trying to have ID taught in the science classroom (they lost: ID was judged to be religion not science).

Intelligent Design: a critique

Many thorough critiques of ID have been published and space allows only two main problems with ID to be emphasised.[29]

Problem One is about what counts as a scientific theory. In reality, ID has none of the characteristics that make it recognisable as science. The purpose of scientific theories in biology is to explain the relationships between all the materials that comprise living matter. Scientific theories must be testable – there must be empirical evidence that can count for or against the theory, otherwise it remains vacuous. A successful theory will, therefore, lead to a research programme which will aim to establish its truth status.

> *ID has none of the characteristics that make it recognisable as science.*

ID fails to count as science by these criteria. First, simply saying that something is "designed" in biology leads to no increase in our understanding of the relationships between the various material components that comprise living matter. Second, labelling a biological entity as "designed" leads to no experimental programme that could be utilised to test the hypothesis, a fact which presumably explains the lack of scientific publications arising from ID writers.

Problem Two comes from the suggestion that it is possible to define certain biological entities as "irreducibly complex" in a meaningful fashion. In reality it just isn't possible. All living matter is composed of thousands of components, all of which need to work together in a coordinated fashion to produce those properties that we associate with life. All the biological "sub-systems" that maintain cell growth and division, including all biochemical pathways, are complex, without exception. It could easily be argued that all of them fall within the ID criteria used to identify an "irreducibly complex" system, since in each and every case the sub-system only functions properly providing all the components are in place. So the ID goal of identifying "designed entities" in biology, detected against a background of "natural entities which science does understand", fails at the first hurdle.[30]

What we have in ID is the "fallacy of large numbers": as soon as you have a multi-component system, then the chances of it coming into being all at once as a fully functional system are remotely small. But, of course, no biologist thinks that's how evolution works. Evolution works incrementally.

In truth, ID looks rather like the old "god-of-the-gaps" argument, except that in this case it might be more accurate to call it the "designer-of-the-gaps" argument. The (flawed) argument here is that "god" provides an explanation for things that science can't (yet) explain. Of course, what invariably happens is that in the fullness of time the gap in scientific knowledge closes and the "god" or "designer" disappears. ID proponents seem to be investing a lot of capital in the fact that we don't (yet) have a detailed understanding of the evolution of many complex entities in biology. But biologists are glad that there are plenty of gaps in scientific knowledge left waiting to be filled – otherwise they would be out of a job! Behe's ID book *Darwin's Black Box* provides many supposed examples of "irreducible complexity" but many of these proposed "gaps" have in fact already been filled in the decade since his book appeared. The biological sciences are moving ahead very quickly at the moment.

conclusion

In truth, ID looks rather like the old "god-of-the-gaps" argument.

Darwinism has often been encountered, at a popular level, cloaked in various philosophical, religious, social or political disguises. The brutal Social Darwinist costume that was prevalent in America in the early 20th century helps explain why the US saw a popular antipathy towards evolution that has not, until recently, been matched on this side of the Atlantic.

Today, however, there is every sign that antipathy towards evolution is growing in the UK. Mercifully, this is not down to a re-emergence of cut-throat Social Darwinism, in which the suffering and annihilation of the weak is somehow rationalised as a good.

Rather, it is because recent decades have seen Darwinian evolution emerge dressed in a new outfit: a reductionist philosophy that reduces morality to self-interest, agency to an illusion, hope to a fantasy, and humans to an irrelevance.

In reality none of that is intrinsic to the theory, but faced with such a bleak vision, many recoil and, over the last twenty years, some have taken refuge in a pseudo-scientific theory, constructed, at least at first as a direct response to this vision.

Recent decades have seen Darwinian evolution emerge dressed in a new outfit: a reductionist philosophy that reduces morality to self-interest, agency to an illusion, hope to a fantasy, and humans to an irrelevance.

The dubious philosophy that drives Intelligent Design (not to mention the dubious theology that drives Young Earth Creationism) in turn provokes modern Darwinians to insist all the more loudly on evolution's truth and its allegedly manifest implications for human nature, morality, religion, etc. And this, in turn, further alienates those who might otherwise be able to accept evolution. A vicious circle is born.

The tragedy in all this is that the battle is entirely unnecessary.

chapter 4 - references

1. Richard Dawkins, *The Selfish Gene* (Oxford University Press, 1976; 2nd edn. 1989), p. 198.

2. Dawkins, *Selfish Gene*, p. 330.

3. Richard Dawkins, "Viruses of the Mind," in *A Devil's Chaplain* (Weidenfeld & Nicolson, 2003), p. 141.

4. Richard Dawkins, *The Humanist* 57, January/February 1997.

5. Dawkins, *Selfish Gene*, p. 270. As Andrew Brown has observed, "This lofty condescension – 'popular, but erroneous' – is difficult for a popular writer to maintain. Who is he to tell us what the erroneous associations of the word 'robot' are?" Andrew Brown, *The Darwin Wars: How Stupid Genes became Selfish Gods* (Simon & Schuster, 1999), p. 40.

6. Richard Dawkins, "In defence of selfish genes", *Philosophy* 56 (1980), pp. 556–573. Andrew Brown: "It's always hard to tell, when words, in his hands, mean more or less what he wants them to. He made his name proclaiming the selfishness of genes, but when this view was challenged he explained that successful 'selfishness' consisted largely in their capacity to co-operate with each other". Brown, *Darwin Wars*, p. 43.

7. Cf. Richard Dawkins debating with John Cornwell, *Today* Programme, 8.30am, 6 September 2007: "I have likened it [religion] to a virus but that's a very special point".

8. Richard Dawkins, "A scientist's case against God," Speech at Edinburgh International Science Festival, 15 April 1992.

9. Dawkins, "Reply to Poole." pp. 45-50.

10. Richard Dawkins, *The Extended Phenotype* (Oxford University Press, 1982), p. 181.

11. Interview with Rowan Williams, *The Guardian*, 21 March 2006.

12. Sir Peter Medawar, "Review of *The Phenomenon of Man*", *Mind* (1961), pp. 99-105.

13. Dawkins, *Blind Watchmaker*, p. 13.

14. Dennett, *Darwin's Dangerous Idea*, p. 82.

15. Dawkins, *Selfish Gene*, p. 270.

16. Dawkins, *Selfish Gene*, p. 10.

17. Richard Dawkins, *Unweaving the Rainbow* (Allen Lane, 1998), p. 308.

18. Edward O Wilson, *Sociobiology* (Harvard University Press, 1975), p. 3.

19. Dennett, *Darwin's Dangerous Idea*, p. 349. Memes are famously invisible, undetectable, unpredictable, unconstructive, unwarranted, and unnecessary things that "leap…from brain to brain" [Dawkins, *Selfish Gene*, p. 192]. It is not immediately clear what purpose they serve – other than to demonise those poor, unfortunate souls who are possessed by the more malign (i.e. religious) kind.

20. Dawkins, *River Out of Eden*, p. 155.

21. David Barash, *Sociology and Behaviour* (Elsevier-North Holland Publishing, 1977).

22. Michael Ghiselin, *The Economy of Nature and the Evolution of Sex* (University of California Press, 1974), p. 247.

23. See, for example, *Alas Poor Darwin: Arguments against Evolutionary Psychology*, Hilary Rose and Steven Rose, eds., (Vintage, 2001).

24. Numbers, *The Creationists*.

25. Philip Johnson, *Testing Darwinism* (Inter-Varsity Press, 1997), pp. 10, 16.

26. Ibid., p. 22.

27. Robert Boyle, "A Free Inquiry into the Vulgarly Received Notion of Nature", in MB Hall (ed.), *Robert Boyle on Natural Philosophy*, (Indiana University Press, 1965), pp. 150-3.

28. William Dembski, *Intelligent Design – the Bridge Between Science and Theology* (IVP Academic, 1999), p. 249.

29. There are a number of key books written by ID proponents, including: Phillip E Johnson, *Darwin on Trial* (Intervarsity Press, 1993; 2nd edn); Phillip E Johnson, *The Wedge of Truth: Splitting the Foundations of Naturalism* (Inter-Varsity Press, 2002); M Behe, *Darwin's Black Box* (The Free Press, 1996); M Behe, *The Edge of Evolution the Search for the Limits of Darwinism* (Free Press, 2007); WA Dembski, *Intelligent Design - the Bridge Between Science and Theology* (IVP Academic, 1999); WA Dembski, *The Design Revolution* (InterVarsity Press, 2004); John C Lennox, *God's Undertaker - Has Science Buried God?* (Lion, 2007). Books providing essays from those pro and anti-ID include: WA Dembski and M Ruse, *Debating Design: From Darwin to DNA* (Cambridge University Press), 2004); Phillip E Johnson and Denis O Lamoureux, eds., *Darwinism Defeated?* (Regent College Publishing, 1999). Books critical of ID from various perspectives include: Denis Alexander, *Creation or Evolution - Do We Have to Choose?* (Monarch, 2008); Francis Collins, *The Language of God* (Pocket Books, 2007); Robert T Pennock, *The Tower of Babel - the Evidence Against the New Creationism* (MIT Press, 1999); Francisco J Ayala, *Darwin and Intelligent Design* (Fortress Press, 2006); Michael Shermer, *Why Darwin Matters: The Case Against Intelligent Design*, (Holt Paperbacks, 2007); Matt Young and Taner Edis, *Why Intelligent Design Fails: A Scientific Critique of the New Creationism* (Rutgers University Press, 2006); John Brockman, *Intelligent Thought: Science versus the Intelligent Design Movement* (Vintage, 2006).

30. For more extensive discussion of these and other points, see Denis Alexander, *Creation or Evolution – Do We Have to Choose?* (Monarch, 2008); Kenneth Miller, *Finding Darwin's God* (Harper, 2007).

Rescuing Darwin

The central argument of this report is that it doesn't have to be like this. Darwin need not, indeed *should not* be caught in the crossfire of a philosophical or theological battle. Religion is not bad science, Genesis is not a primitive *Origin of Species*, and Darwinism does not necessitate atheism, any more than it reduces morality to "underlying selfishness"[1] or the mind to "a…habitat for memes".[2]

To rescue Darwin from this conflict, two key issues need to be addressed: the first theological, the second scientific. First, the idea that "religion is a scientific theory" needs to be debunked; specifically those passages of the Bible which some take to be literal or proto-scientific descriptions of the origins of life and the universe need to be shown to be otherwise. Second, those "scientific" arguments that insist that evolution somehow necessitates atheism and reductionism need to be shown to be unwarranted. This chapter tackles both questions.

Genesis in history

Five years before he killed himself, Robert FitzRoy, erstwhile captain of the *Beagle*, attended the famous British Association for the Advancement of Science meeting in Oxford.

In the excitement of the debate, he was seen to stand up and, holding his Bible aloft, entreat the assembled audience to believe God's holy word rather than that of a mere human on the questions of creation.[3]

Writing in the third century, the theologian Origen was scornful of those who read the opening chapter literally.

FitzRoy himself had not always been so rigid and literal in his understanding of Genesis – he had discussed new geological theories openly with Darwin when on the *Beagle* – but by 1860 he was convinced that science was in direct competition with religion, and *The Origin of Species* with Genesis chapter 1.

He was not to know that such a literal, "competitive" reading of the creation story was a comparatively modern phenomenon. Writing in the third century, the theologian Origen was scornful of those who read the opening chapter literally.

> What man of intelligence, I ask, will consider that the first and second and the third day, in which there are said to be both morning and evening, existed without sun and moon and stars, while the first day was even without a heaven? And who could be found so silly as to believe that God, after the manner of a farmer "planted trees in a paradise eastward in Eden"…I do not think anyone will doubt that these are figurative expressions which indicate certain mysteries through a semblance of history.[4]

Origen was not the only Church Father to adopt this approach. Jerome, Gregory of Nyssa, and Ambrose were all flexible in their reading of the text. Augustine's famous commentary from the early fifth century, *The Literal Interpretation of Genesis*, was not at all literal in today's popular understanding of that term. Indeed, Augustine was particularly hard on those who damaged the Bible's credibility by using it ignorantly to pronounce on unrelated issues, such as "the motion and orbit of the stars…their size and relative positions…the predictable eclipses of the sun and moon, the cycles of the years and the seasons…the kinds of animals, shrubs, stones, and so forth."[5] Augustine wrote that:

> It is a disgraceful and dangerous thing for an infidel to hear a Christian, presumably giving the meaning of Holy Scripture, talking nonsense on these topics … [Such] reckless and incompetent expounders of Holy Scripture bring untold trouble and sorrow on their wiser brethren when they are caught in one of their mischievous false opinions and are taken to task by those who are not bound by the authority of our sacred books. For then, to defend their utterly foolish and obviously untrue statements, they will try to call upon Holy Scripture for proof and even recite from memory many passages which they think support their position, although they understand neither what they say nor the things about which they make assertion.

Augustine was particularly hard on those who damaged the Bible's credibility by using it ignorantly to pronounce on unrelated issues.

In understanding the central role of figurative language in the early chapters of Genesis, the Church Fathers were following an already established Jewish tradition of creative and highly flexible interpretation. Early Jewish commentaries on Genesis favoured symbolic readings of the early chapters. Many of the early rabbinic writings were of the view that God created everything instantaneously rather than in any particular period of time. The Targums, the Aramaic translations of and commentaries on the Hebrew Scriptures with which Jesus and St Paul would have been familiar, were extremely flexible in how they read (and what they read into) these verses. The highly influential Alexandrian Jew, Philo, a contemporary of both Jesus and Paul, explained at some length how the days of creation, the "image of God", Adam and Eve, and the garden of Eden were all "intended symbolically rather than literally", being "no mythical fictions…but modes of making ideas visible".[6]

> Early Jewish commentaries on Genesis favoured symbolic readings of the early chapters.

Such figurative readings continued into the Middle Ages, in the work of rabbis such as Rashi, Maimonides and Gersonides, and some Christian theologians such as Nicholas of Lyra. In the process, allegorical readings of Biblical texts became excessive and it was in reaction to this trend that the Reformers downplayed moral, allegorical and anagogical interpretations (representing three strands of the mediaeval *Quadriga* or "fourfold sense of scripture") in favour of a literal reading alone.[7] Even then the pattern wasn't universal. Calvin, for example, favoured a literal interpretation but recognised that Moses, whom he believed authored Genesis, had "adapt[ed] his discourse to common usage".[8]

Genesis today

Today, scholars understand Genesis not through the lens of excessive metaphorical speculation favoured by so many early and mediaeval theologians, but by means of close textual analysis conducted in the light of the contemporary ancient Near Eastern culture and literature.

That textual analysis has shown that Genesis 1-3 comprises two stories, commonly known as the Priestly (1.1–2.4a) and the Yahwist (2.4b-3.24). The former, which is the better known story of creation, is itself structured in such a way as to offer readers a clue as to how to interpret it. Early on, in verse 2, the writer describes the earth as "formless" and "empty". Thereafter, the first half of God's activity (days 1-3 in verses 3-13[9]) gives *form* to the creation, separating light from darkness, water above from water below, and sea from dry land, and the second half (days 4-6 in verses 14-31) gives *content*, in the form of lights in the sky, life in the sea and air, and life on land.

Such a structure suggests that the text simply cannot be read as if it were a scientific text. Instead, when we read the early chapters of Genesis carefully and compare them with other ancient Near Eastern creation stories, what emerges is a text that is not so much interested in explaining *how* the universe came into being as one that outlines how we should understand it, a text that, at its simplest, deals with meaning rather than fact.[10] It is, in essence, a piece of *theological polemic*, a critique of contemporary worldviews, in the words of one evangelical scholar "a conscious and deliberate antimythical polemic which meant an undermining of the prevailing mythological cosmologies."[11]

This can be seen in a number of ways. The story is resolutely monotheistic, unremarkable to us but rather incendiary within an ancient Near Eastern polytheistic culture. Unlike other creation stories of the region, the biblical one does not begin with a "theogony", explaining the origin of the gods. Rather, it is a simple "cosmogony", provocatively assuming that God is one and pre-existent without bothering to argue the fact (and thus of little relevance to the age-old "Who made God?" debate).[12]

> *When we read the early chapters of Genesis carefully what emerges is "a conscious and deliberate antimythical polemic which meant an undermining of the prevailing mythological cosmologies."*

Second, the story describes the creation not of the "Sun" and "Moon" (in verse 16) but of "the greater light" and "the lesser light". Hebrew, like other Semitic languages, had perfectly good words for Sun and Moon but these were also the names of gods worshipped in contemporary cultures. The description of these heavenly bodies as "lights" rather than by name deliberately demystifies them, undermining the supposed divinity of other gods.

Third, the story uses the rare word *ba'ra* meaning, broadly, to "create without effort". The Hebrew Bible only ever uses this verb to describe God's creative action and it is used only three times in Genesis chapter 1. Two of the uses, in verse 1 (relating to "the heavens and the earth") and in verse 27 (relating to "mankind in his own image") are understandable, but it is not immediately obvious why the verb should occur in verse 21, relating to "the great creatures of the sea".

The reason appears to be that, in ancient Near Eastern creation stories, such great sea creatures commonly symbolised the powers of chaos, which the gods had to wrestle and overcome in order to create and bring about order. The use of *ba'ra* in verse 21 deliberately rejects this worldview, asserting that the Hebrew God did not need to do battle with any such semi-divine monster in order to create and that, therefore, the forces of chaos are not a threat.

The attendant point here is that "Mesopotamian religion has been described as 'anxiety-ridden' because there was always the fear that the cosmos would collapse back into chaos", the fear that the forces of chaos were merely suppressed rather than subjugated.[13] The text seems to be deliberately countering such a view, stressing that the order of creation is permanent and assured, rather than dependent on sacrifices to the gods or divine whim.

This point is directly linked to a fourth, relating to the Hebrew word *tehôm* in verse 2. This word, usually translated "deep", is used in the text in a "depersonalised" and "non-mythical" sense, understood as "a passive, powerless, inanimate element in God's creation."[14] Again, this would seem unremarkable but for the fact that, just as the great sea creatures were understood as symbolic of the forces of chaos, so were the waters they inhabited.

Genesis rejects this notion of chaotic forces outside God's control. *Tehôm* is not the pre-existent, primeval ocean of other ancient Near Eastern creation stories. It is devoid of mythical connotations and independent power. In the words of the theologian Gerhard Hasel:

> In stating the conditions in which the cosmos existed before God commanded that light should spring forth, the author of Genesis rejected explicitly contemporary mythological notions by using the term tehôm, whose cognates are deeply mythological in their usage in ancient Near Eastern creation speculations, in such a way that it is not only non-mythical in content but anti mythical in purpose...It appears inescapable to recognize here again a conscious polemic against the battle myth.[15]

Other, similar points may be made. Ancient Near Eastern creation stories are replete with tales of how heaven and earth were created by an act of separation. The Babylonian epic *Enûma elish*, for example, tells how the god Marduk formed heaven and earth out of the upper and lower parts respectively of the slain monster Tiamat, and the deep from her blood. An act of separation is present in Genesis (verse 6) but "any notion of a combat, struggle or force is absent."[16]

Similarly, although the idea of creation by divine word was not uncommon at the time, that divine word was often a specific, almost magical utterance, an ancient "abracadabra", as opposed to the almost casual, effortless words of Genesis chapter 1.

Humans in ancient Near Eastern creation stories were the slaves of the gods, created to build their houses (temples) and provide them with food (sacrifices).[17] In contrast, humanity in Genesis is neither an afterthought nor a slave, but the conclusion of the creative process, bearing God's image, and with a particular duty to act as God's vice-regent on earth, caring for the earth and its creatures. Uniquely among ancient creation stories, the God of Genesis does not create through having sex. The examples mount up.

Such analysis does not indicate that the interpretation of the creation stories is settled. Indeed, to suggest they ever could be is to misunderstand fundamentally the practice of biblical studies, where, like science, work is always on-going.

What they do point towards is an ordered, reliable creation, in which humans are significant and have morally-serious roles to play, ruled over by one God who is not threatened or challenged by other would-be deities or any intrinsically chaotic nature within creation itself.

Discerning such a message from the text is more than mere theological sophistry. It was, of course, the monotheism of Genesis rather than the polytheism of rival Ancient Near Eastern cultures that came to dominate medieval and early-modern Europe. The Genesis stories were, as we have noted, in no sense intended to be science but they did help the birth of science (and, ironically, the scientific literature with which they were subsequently confused).

Early European scientists were for the most part deeply devout, spurred on in their work by their specifically Christian convictions, many rooted in Genesis, that creation was ordered, rational and comprehensible, and that by studying it they would better understand and glorify God. The early chapters of Genesis might not be science but it is quite possible that without them science would not have developed when, where and how it did.

> *Genesis 1-3 is no more a "scientific" account of how life developed, than the Torah is a study of ethical origins.*

Perhaps most importantly for the argument of this essay, this reading of Genesis does clearly indicate what the text is *not*. Genesis 1-3 is no more a "scientific" account of how life developed, than the Torah is a study of ethical origins, the gospels a philosophical defence of miracles, or religion itself an "explanation for facts about the universe and life".[18]

Those who believe otherwise are guilty of imposing upon the relevant texts a modernist mind-set alien to the world of the original authors. If religious believers and atheists alike can recognise this, one of the main obstacles to recognising Darwinism for what it is, and Darwin for what he achieved, can be removed.

> *The atheistic interpretation of evolution is based on a fundamental misunderstanding about the aims and scope of science.*

But only one of the obstacles. The other – the idea that evolution necessitates the death of God (and indeed, in some regards, the death of humanity) – remains.

rescuing evolution

Does evolution necessitate atheism? Despite the fact that only 37% of the UK population think that "humans evolved by a process of evolution which removes any need for God", this is a peculiarly widespread and persistent belief, propounded by creationists on one side and a small number of highly vocal atheists on the other. However, just as the creationist position rests on a misconception of what Genesis is and what it is telling the reader, the atheistic interpretation of evolution is based on a fundamental misunderstanding about the aims and scope of science.

Reductionism is essential as a methodological approach in science.

understanding science

In the middle ages and early modern period, the term "science" was used to refer to virtually any body of accurate, constructed knowledge. Theology was famously known then as the "queen of the sciences" because it was deemed to encompass all other forms of knowledge. What we now know as "science" was more commonly called "natural philosophy" and those who pursued it were known as "natural philosophers". The word "scientist" is of relatively recent origin, invented in 1834 by the Anglican cleric, William Whewell, who was Master of Trinity College and one of the great polymaths of 19th century Cambridge.

Today we define modern science as "an organised endeavour to explain the properties of the physical world by means of empirically testable theories constructed by a research community trained in specialised techniques". [19]

There are certain key properties that are characteristic of the methods of modern science, which help us to know that we're talking about science and not something else. For example:

1. Science, in its methodologies, excludes questions of ultimate purpose, value and significance. By contrast, Aristotelian science included final causality as one of the explanatory features of nature. As we have already noted, empirical science only really began to take off in the 16th and 17th centuries as it became more modest in its ambitions and began to exclude the consideration of final causes.

2. Science looks for testable hypotheses.

3. Science aims at formulating generalisations about the properties of things whenever possible, the highest levels of which are called "laws".

4. Science values mathematics highly and incorporates mathematical assessment whenever appropriate and feasible.

5. Science aims at objectivity and downplays the role of the scientific observer, deliberately excluding the personal.

6. Scientific knowledge aims to be publicly observable and repeatable. It is only taken seriously within the scientific community following publication in peer-reviewed journals. In a sense, you can define science by what is contained within the pages of scientific journals.

The goal of the scientific community is to generate a body of reliable, constructed knowledge that is deliberately restricted in its ambition to explain the physical properties of things. Science achieves clarity only at the price of looking away from the layers of nature available to other kinds of experience.

The problem with this ultra-reductionist view of science is that it sees the scientific story as the only story worth telling.

Reductionism is essential as a methodological approach in science. If you want to understand how a car engine works, you take it to bits. But extreme reductionism claims that it is the bits themselves that represent the "real" story, not the bits functioning together as a whole. Extreme reductionism is often identified by the rhetoric of "only", "simply", "just", "nothing but" and "no more than". Thus the late Francis Crick, co-discoverer of the structure of DNA, wrote that:

The Astonishing Hypothesis is that 'You', your joys and your sorrows, your memories and your ambitions, your sense of personal identity and free will, are in fact no more than the behaviour of a vast assembly of nerve cells and their associated molecules.[20]

Science simply cannot (by its legitimate methods) adjudicate the issue of God's possible superintendence of nature. We neither affirm nor deny it; we simply can't comment on it as scientists.

The problem with this ultra-reductionist view of science is that it sees the scientific story as the *only* story worth telling, implying that there are no other valid stories that can be told about the world or about our lives. This is a curiously flat view of the world, when all that we know about our own experience suggests that our lives are multi-dimensional, and that we need many different types of explanation to make sense of the world. The scientific approach is important but questions of purpose, meaning, ethics, beauty, history, literature and love are equally, arguably *more* important and, crucially, beyond science's capacity to answer. This gets to the heart of why the argument that evolution (or, indeed, science) demands atheism is wrong. In the words of the late Stephen Jay Gould:

Science simply cannot (by its legitimate methods) adjudicate the issue of God's possible superintendence of nature. We neither affirm nor deny it; we simply can't comment on it as scientists.[21]

A more useful way to picture the relationship between scientific and other forms of knowledge is to envisage the complex reality that we experience in our daily lives as being like a cube sliced into many layers. Each layer represents a different approach to understanding the world around us. The scientific level of understanding tells us how things work and where they come from; the moral and ethical level addresses what we ought to do in the world; the aesthetic level gives insight into our understanding and appreciation of beauty; the personal level addresses the ways in which we construct our biographies, and so forth. At the religious level the key questions are: Does life have any purpose in an ultimate sense? Does God exist? Why is there a universe anyway? Or, in the words of Stephen Hawking, referring to the equations that define the fine-tuning of the physical constants that render the universe feasible, "what breathes fire into the equations?"[22]

> *The theory of evolution by natural selection is a supremely elegant and parsimonious explanation of the relevant biological data. But it cannot adjudicate on the existence of God any more than it can on the reasons for the Battle of Hastings, the literary merits of Paradise Lost, or formation of the Andromeda Galaxy.*

These various explanatory levels are in no sense rivals to each other. We need them *all* to do justice to our experience as human agents. Nor should it be thought that "real knowledge" belongs to just one layer, such as science, whereas all the other layers are a matter of personal opinion. Each branch of human knowledge has its own well-established criteria for rational justification: legal beliefs require legal justifications; historical beliefs require historical justifications, and so forth. Well-justified belief, which includes religious beliefs, is not just the provenance of science.

Darwin's theory provides an excellent example of the way that a scientific theory can bring coherence to a broad array of disparate data. As the late evolutionary biologist Ernst Mayr has written:

The theory of evolution is quite rightly called the greatest unifying theory in biology. The diversity of organisms, similarities and differences between kinds of organisms, patterns of distribution and behaviour, adaptation and interaction, all this was merely a bewildering chaos of facts until given meaning by the evolutionary theory.[23]

The theory of evolution by natural selection is a supremely elegant and parsimonious explanation of the relevant biological data. But it cannot adjudicate on the existence of God any more than it can on the reasons for the Battle of Hastings, the literary merits of *Paradise Lost*, or formation of the Andromeda Galaxy. Yet these other types of non-scientific explanation can, using criteria appropriate for the question in hand, provide explanatory "maps" of reality just as persuasive as evolution by natural selection.

are theism and evolution *compatible*?

If science cannot, by legitimate means, adjudicate on the God question, can it argue that the particular "level" of reality that it explores, in this case, biology, is somehow *incompatible* with the existence of a loving, all-powerful God?

> *The objection that evolution is a "wasteful" process doesn't bear close examination.*

It is this claim that lies at the heart – beneath the many layers of colourful rhetoric – of "scientific" (and, indeed, some religious) objections to evolution. Are the different levels of explanation in our "cube" analogy really compatible, ask the atheistic evolutionists? Surely God would not have chosen to create by such a lengthy process as evolution, apparently random and involving so much suffering? We might agree that evolution cannot disprove God, yet still feel that the two sit uncomfortably together.

In essence this accusation comprises three separate elements: that evolution is too wasteful, too chancy and too painful to be reconciled with God.

Regarding the first, the objection that evolution is a "wasteful" process doesn't bear close examination. The staggering size of the universe with its 10^{11} galaxies each containing about 10^{11} stars provides a useful background for thinking about the subject. As we now understand, the universe *needs* to be this old (and therefore this vast) in order for elements such as carbon and oxygen, essential for life, to be formed.

> *"Wasteful" is a slippery and subjective word, and we need to be very careful to avoid inappropriate and over-sentimental anthropomorphisms when using it.*

In a similar fashion, just as the heavier elements, the stars, and their orbiting planets need billions of years to come into being, so complex life needs billions of years in order to evolve. It takes about 3.8 billion years, years of extraordinary fruitfulness and diversity, to make a human being. Who are we to call that a waste?

"Wasteful", then, is a slippery and subjective word, and we need to be very careful to avoid inappropriate and over-sentimental anthropomorphisms when using it. What does "waste" actually mean? Are billions of years and billions of light years "wasteful" if they are necessary for the creation of planets like our own? Why should millions of years of biological growth and variety be deemed "wasteful"? Is a species wasted simply because it doesn't exist when we happen to be alive? Is an organism a waste simply because it doesn't reproduce or reach a ripe old age?

The idea that the size of the universe or the history of life is somehow "wasteful" seems to owe something to the idea that God should behave like the manager of a modern industrial plant, doing everything with the utmost efficiency, using the minimum of resources and in the shortest possible time. But why is that picture the right one? All analogies of divine work are inadequate but it is surely more appropriate to see God as a creative artist than an industrial manager. That is certainly the analogy preferred in the Bible.

If the accusation of wastefulness is dubious, what about the question of "chance"? Happily this is where atheists and theists find themselves in agreement. Richard Dawkins states very clearly that one of the main reasons he wrote his book *The Blind Watchmaker* was "to destroy this eagerly believed myth that Darwinism is a theory of 'chance'".[24] Taken as a whole, evolution is not a chance process but one that is tightly constrained and organised by the physical parameters of planet earth.

It is true that the generation of genetic diversity does occur by chance, in the sense that the changes that occur do not anticipate the future needs of the organism, and cannot be predicted in advance, as they involve random mutations in the DNA. But natural selection subsequently acts as a tight filter, leading to the differential reproductive success that ensures that, on average, it is the fittest genomes that are passed on to subsequent generations.

How this works out in practice is well illustrated by the phenomenon of "convergence". Convergence refers to the repeated evolution in independent lineages of the same biochemical pathway, organ or structure. Life has a habit of constantly "navigating" its way to the same (or very similar) "solutions". This has been recognised for a long time in evolutionary biology and has recently been described in impressive detail by Simon Conway Morris, Professor of Palaeobiology at Cambridge University, in his book *Life's Solution: Inevitable Humans in a Lonely Universe*.[25]

Conway Morris remarks that "convergence offers a metaphor as to how evolution navigates the combinatorial immensities of biological 'hyperspace'"[26]. To take the classic example, compound and camera eyes taken together have evolved more than 20 different times during the course of evolution. If you live in a planet of light and darkness, then you need eyes – so eyes are what you're going to get. Similarly, wings, legs, claws, teeth, brains, and much else besides have evolved time and time and time again. "The evolutionary routes are many, but the destinations are limited." [27]

Conway Morris recognises the accusation of "chance" that animates the evolutionary arguments against theism: evolution is a random and directionless process that cannot be reconciled with God:

> [It is] now widely thought that the history of life is little more than a contingent muddle punctuated by disastrous mass extinctions that in spelling the doom of one group so open the doors of opportunity to some other mob of lucky chancers…Rerun the tape of the history of life…and the end result will be an utterly different biosphere. Most notably there will be nothing remotely like a human. [28]

Yet this, he observes, is badly wrong.

> What we know of evolution suggests the exact reverse: convergence is ubiquitous and the constraints of life make the emergence of the various biological properties [e.g. intelligence] very probable, if not inevitable. [29]

Evolution, then, is nothing like as chancy a process as is popularly believed. There is certainly a random element within it but natural selection and the physical properties of our planet mean that there are many tight filters involved in the process. In essence, there are only so many ways of fighting, feeling, feeding and reproducing and species repeatedly find their way to them. Rewind and replay the tape of life and you would get a picture that was strangely similar to the one we have today, one in which organisms flew, crawled, heard, smelt, watched, and perhaps even walked, talked, thought and loved.

Such an account seems wholly consistent with the theistic account of a God who has intentions and purposes for the world. "Chance", like "waste", is not what it first appears.

Pain is essential for our survival. Without it we would be munching on broken glass, walking on broken legs, and ignoring disastrous infections.

A similar argument applies to the third accusation, that evolution is too painful a path for God to have used. We live in a world in which biology (like astrophysics) is a "package deal". Life has necessary costs. Organisms cannot survive without sensing changes in their environment and in their own bodies, which in turn necessitates pain. Pain is essential for our survival. Without it we would be munching on broken glass, walking on broken legs, and ignoring disastrous infections.

This is illustrated very vividly by those individuals with a complete inability to feel pain due to selective mutations.[30] In one case a patient placed knives through his arms and walked on burning coals but experienced no pain, dying before his 14th birthday by jumping off a house roof. We need pain to say alive.

> *Theists do not derive their theology solely from studying nature. They recognise another source of legitimate "data".*

It is, however, at the intersection of the accusations of "chance" and "pain" that there lies the most serious challenge to the theist. Those same mutations that are the engine of biological diversity are also the mutations that cause painful and fatal genetic diseases, including cancer. If anything is incompatible with a loving God, surely this is?

To some extent theists can point to the realities of the biological narrative in their defence here. Without genetic variation we would not exist, because evolution would not happen, not to mention the rest of the rich biological diversity that helps make this planet so wonderful.

Yet there remains the accusation that if pain and genetic disease do cause so much suffering in life – and if this life is all there is – then doesn't it all seem a bit pointless? Suffering does, as a matter of fact, invoke great acts of compassion and altruism, not to mention endurance on the part of the sufferer. Yet if all those acts are simply going to be obliterated in the onward march of time, as our sun's energy eventually runs out and all life on the planet ceases, then doesn't it all seem rather meaningless?

> *The present world is a place in which we grow morally and spiritually, where suffering is not final, but can be healed and redeemed; a place where love rather than death has the final word.*

This is where it is important to emphasise that theists do not derive their theology solely from studying nature. They recognise another source of legitimate "data", data that they could not accumulate simply by their own efforts, and which is crucial for addressing this accusation. For Christians, that understanding of life and of God is derived supremely from the life, teachings, death and resurrection of Jesus Christ. In the words of Rowan Williams:

Christians understand the primary location of God's revealing Word to be the history of God's people and above all the history of Jesus Christ, whom we acknowledge as the Word made flesh, to which the Bible is the authoritative and irreplaceable witness.[31]

This is key as it changes the perspective on the data gathered from other sources, such as from studying nature or the cosmos. If, as Christians believe, this present world finds its fulfilment in a "new heaven and a new earth", no longer time-bound, then the situation looks strikingly different. It implies that the present world is less like a Holiday Camp than a Boot Camp, a place in which we grow morally and spiritually, where suffering is not final, but can be healed and redeemed; a place where love rather than death has the final word.

No-one is naïve enough to think that such reflections give final answers to the problem of suffering in the evolutionary process, and there is a wealth of literature that discusses such questions in much greater depth than space allows here.[32] Theological reflection – like science and biblical studies – is an on-going, reflective discipline, only closed and absolutist in the minds of fundamentalist believers and some equally fundamentalist atheists.

But such reflections do offer tentative and hopeful answers to the accusation of incompatibility that evolution can lay at theism's door. The idea that this life in all its biological complexity is a necessary preparation for a future one casts a very different light on the evolutionary story.

Evolution cannot, then, pronounce on the God question in the way that some of its more vocal proponents believe, but it can lay meaningful challenges at theism's door. The most significant of these – that evolution is too wasteful, chancy or painful a process to be worthy of God – need to be taken seriously. Although such challenges tend not to be as momentous as some claim, they do provide opportunities for genuine reflection and debate. And that, if conducted in a spirit of respect and courtesy, benefits everyone.

chapter 5 - references

1. Barash, *Sociology and Behaviour*.

2. Dennett, *Darwin's Dangerous Idea*, p. 349.

3. Janet Browne, *Charles Darwin: The Power of Place, Volume 2 of a biography* (Jonathan Cape, 2003), p. 123.

4. Origen, *First Principles*, Bk.4, ch.3 (SPCK, 1936; trans. G. Butterworth).

5. Augustine, *On the Literal Meaning of Genesis* (Newman Press, 1982; trans. JH Taylor), pp. 42ff.

6. Philo, "On the Creation", 13–14, in *Philo: Volume 1* (Loeb Classical Library, 1929; trans. FH Colson & GH Whitaker).

7. Broadly speaking, the literal outlined the plain sense of the text, the allegorical informed Christians what to believe, the moral told them what to do, and the anagogical what to hope for. See Alister McGrath, *Christian Theology: An Introduction* (Blackwell, 1994), pp. 163-181.

8. John Calvin, *A Commentary on Genesis*, (Banner of Truth, 1967; trans. J King).

9. The verse numbers were, of course, added centuries later.

10. In doing so, it fits well with the distinction between science and religion outlined by the noted 20th century evolutionary biologist Theodosius Dobzhansky: "Science and religion deal with different aspects of existence. If one dares to overschematize for the sake of clarity, one may say that these are the aspect of fact and the aspect of meaning." See Theodosius Dobzhansky, *The Biology of Ultimate Concern* (Fontana, 1971), p. 96.

11. Gerhard F Hasel, "The Polemic Nature of the Genesis Cosmology", *Evangelical Quarterly* 46 (1974), pp. 81-102.

12. The question of whether God is in fact pre-existent and creates *ex nihilo*, or whether he creates from pre-existing matter is a live one, hinging on how one understands (and translates) the original text. See Paul Copan and William Lane Craig, *Creation out of Nothing: A Biblical, Philosophical, and Scientific Exploration* (Baker Academic, 2004).

13. Ernest Lucas, "Science and the Bible: Are They Incompatible?" in *Science & Christian Belief* 17 (2005), pp. 137–154.

14. Hasel, "Polemic Nature", p. 84.

15. Hasel, "Polemic Nature", p. 85.

16. Hasel, "Polemic Nature", p. 88.

17. Hasel, "Polemic Nature", p. 90.

18. Dawkins, "A Reply to Poole", pp. 45-50.

19. Denis Alexander, *Science, Friend or Foe?* Cambridge Papers, September 1995.

20. F Crick, *The Astonishing Hypothesis* (Simon & Schuster, 1994), p. 3.

21. Stephen Jay Gould, "Impeaching a Self-Appointed Judge" in *Scientific American* 267 (1) (1992), pp. 118-121.

22. Stephen Hawking, *A Brief History of Time* (Bantam Press, 10th anniversary edition, 1998), p. 209.

23. E Mayr, *Towards a New Philosophy of Biology - Observations of an Evolutionist* (Harvard University Press, 1988).

24. Dawkins, *Blind Watchmaker*, pp. xiii-xvii.

25. Simon Conway Morris, *Life's Solution – Inevitable Humans in a Lonely Universe* (Cambridge University Press, 2003).

26. Conway Morris, *Life's Solution*.

27. Conway Morris, *Life's Solution*, p. 145.

28. Conway Morris, *Life's Solution*, pp. 283-284.

29. Conway Morris, *Life's Solution*, pp. 283-284.

30. JJ Cox et al, "An SCN9A Channelopathy Causes Congenital Inability to Experience Pain", *Nature* 444 (2006) pp. 894-898; SG Waxman "A Channel Sets the Gain on Pain", *Nature* 444 (2006) pp. 831-832.

31. Rowan Williams, "A Common Word for the Common Good", 14 July 2008

32. Denis Alexander, *Creation or Evolution – Do We Have to Choose?*, (Monarch, 2008); Kenneth Miller, *Finding Darwin's God,* (Harper, 2007); AR Peacocke, *Evolution: the Disguised Friend of Faith?* (Templeton Foundation Press, 2004); A Farrer, *Love Almighty and Ills Unlimited* (Collins, 1962); R Swinburne, *Providence and the Problem of Evil* (Oxford University Press, 1998); H Blocher, *Evil and the Cross* (Kregel, 1994); B Hebblethwaite, *Evil, Suffering and Religion* (SPCK, 2000); MM Adams and RM Adams, *The Problem of Evil* (Oxford University Press, 1990); MM Adams, *Horrendous Evils and the Goodness of God* (Cornell University Press, 1999).

conclusion

One word more on "designed laws" & "undesigned results". I see a bird which I want for food, take my gun & kill it, I do this designedly. - An innocent & good man stands under tree & is killed by flash of lightning. Do you believe (& I really sh[oul]d like to hear) that God designedly killed this man? Many or most persons do believe this; I can't & don't.[1]

Darwin's correspondence with Asa Gray was a model of how to discuss evolution and theology.

For all that he was unable to reconcile evolution by natural selection with his understanding of God, Darwin was equally unconvinced by the idea of a "blind, brute" universe.

Gray was Professor of Natural History at Harvard University, a post he held for 46 years. He was President of the American Academy of Arts and Sciences and president of the American Association for the Advancement of Science. He was also a devout and thoughtful Christian, describing himself as "one who is scientifically, and in his own fashion, a Darwinian, philosophically a convinced theist, and religiously an acceptor of the "creed commonly called the Nicene", as the exponent of the Christian faith."[2] He corresponded with Darwin for decades and was responsible, above anyone else, for promoting and defending evolution in America.

Gray and Darwin saw eye-to-eye on many issues but disagreed over what role, if any, God had in evolution. Gray saw God guiding it step-by-step, variation-by-variation. Darwin rejected this, arguing that such a view was inelegant, unscientific, and theologically questionable, implicating God in all sorts of affairs, from the tiny ("a swallow snaps up a gnat") to the tragic (a "good man...is killed by flash of lightning")."If the death of neither man or gnat are designed, I see no good reason to believe that their first birth or production sh[oul]d be necessarily designed," he reasoned.[3]

Yet that was not the end of the affair. For all that he was unable to reconcile evolution by natural selection with his understanding of God, Darwin was equally unconvinced by the idea of a "blind, brute" universe. "As I said before," he continued to Gray, "I cannot persuade myself that electricity acts, that the tree grows, that man aspires to loftiest conceptions all from blind, brute force." He was, he recognised, somewhat confused, signing the letter, "Your muddled & affectionate friend, Ch. Darwin."

In their correspondence we see everything that the debate surrounding evolution and God should be, and everything it has lost. The protagonists are gracious, respectful and thoughtful. They are persuaded of their own views but open to criticism. They occupy the middle ground between aggressive atheism and dogmatic religiosity, and explore possibilities without rancour or ill-feeling.

If we can revisit our popular misconceptions relating to the message of Genesis and the true implications of evolution by natural selection, we too might rediscover a dialogue that is equally courteous and fruitful.

conclusion - references

1. Letter to Asa Gray, 3 July 1860.

2. Asa Gray, *Darwiniana: essays and reviews pertaining to Darwinism* (New York, 1876), p. 5.

3. Letter to Asa Gray, 3 July 1860.

further reading

On Darwin

Janet Browne, *Charles Darwin: Voyaging, Volume 1 of a biography* (Jonathan Cape, 1995).
Janet Browne, *Charles Darwin: The Power of Place, Volume 2 of a biography* (Jonathan Cape, 2003).
Charles Darwin, *Autobiographies* (Penguin Classics, 2002).
Adrian Desmond and James Moore, *Darwin* (Penguin, 1992).

On Darwin and God

Nick Spencer, *Darwin and God* (SPCK, 2009).

On God after Darwin

Denis Alexander, *Rebuilding the Matrix – Science and Faith in the 21st Century* (Lion, 2001).
JH Brooke, *Science & Religion - Some Historical Perspectives* (Cambridge University Press, 1991).
D Livingstone, *Darwin's Forgotten Defenders* (Scottish Academic Press, 1987).
James Moore, *The Post-Darwinian Controversies: A Study of the Protestant Struggle to Come to Terms with Darwin in Great Britain and America, 1870-1900* (Cambridge University Press, 1981).

On Darwinism and God

Denis Alexander, *Creation or Evolution: Do we have to choose?* (Monarch Books, 2008).
Francis Collins, *The Language of God* (Free Press, 2006).
Alister McGrath, *Dawkins' God: Genes, Memes and the Meaning of Life* (Blackwell, 2004).
Michael Ruse, *Can a Darwinian be a Christian?: The Relationship between Science and Religion* (Cambridge University Press, 2004).

On Intelligent Design

Francisco J Ayala, *Darwin and Intelligent Design* (Fortress Press, 2006).
M Behe, *The Edge of Evolution the Search for the Limits of Darwinism* (Free Press, 2007).
WA Dembski, *The Design Revolution* (InterVarsity Press, 2004).
WA Dembski and M Ruse, *Debating Design: From Darwin to DNA* (Cambridge University Press, 2004).
Phillip E Johnson, *The Wedge of Truth: Splitting the Foundations of Naturalism* (Inter-Varsity Press, 2002).
Phillip E Johnson and Denis O Lamoureux, eds., *Darwinism Defeated?* (Regent College Publishing, 1999).
Michael Shermer, *Why Darwin Matters: The Case Against Intelligent Design* (Holt Paperbacks, 2007).

On Darwinian evolution

Richard Dawkins, *The Selfish Gene* (Oxford University Press, 1976; 2nd edn. 1989).
Richard Dawkins, *The Blind Watchmaker* (Longman, 1986).
Richard Dawkins, *River Out of Eden* (Weidenfeld & Nicolson, 1995).
Richard Dawkins, *The Ancestor's Tale*, (Phoenix, 2005).
Daniel Dennett, *Darwin's Dangerous Idea* (Simon & Schuster, 1995).
Steve Jones, *Almost like a whale: The 'Origin of Species' Updated* (Doubleday, 1999).
Hilary Rose and Steven Rose, eds., *Alas Poor Darwin: Arguments against evolutionary psychology* (Vintage, 2001).
C Zimmer, *Where Did We Come From?'* (Apple Press, 2006).

On Genesis

Walter Brueggeman, *Genesis: Interpretation Commentary* (John Knox Press, 1982).
Ernest Lucas, *Can we believe Genesis today?: The Bible and the Questions of Science* (Inter-Varsity Press, 2001).
Gordon Wenham, *Genesis 1-15: Word Biblical Commentary* (Word Books, 1987).
Claus Westermann, *Genesis 1-11* (SPCK, 1984).

C O M M O N S   D E E D

Attribution-NonCommercial-NoDerivs 2.5

You are free:

- to copy, distribute, display, and perform the work

Under the following conditions:

Attribution. You must attribute the work in the manner specified by the author or licensor.

Noncommercial. You may not use this work for commercial purposes.

No Derivative Works. You may not alter, transform, or build upon this work.

- For any reuse or distribution, you must make clear to others the license terms of this work.
- Any of these conditions can be waived if you get permission from the copyright holder.

Your fair use and other rights are in no way affected by the above.

Your fair use and other rights are in no way affected by the above.